INTEGRATING
PRIMITIVE REFLEXES
THROUGH PLAY AND EXERCISE

AN INTERACTIVE GUIDE TO THE
TONIC LABYRINTHINE REFLEX (TLR)

FOR PARENTS, TEACHERS
AND SERVICE PROVIDERS

KOKEB GIRMA MCDONALD, OTR/L
OCCUPATIONAL THERAPIST REGISTERED AND LICENSED

ISBN: 978-1-7342143-38

Editor – Bernice Martin Delcorde
Illustrator – Alex Lopez
Formatter – Jen Henderson at Wild Words Formatting

DEDICATION

MY HUSBAND

Thank you for your love and support. Your dedication to making a positive difference in the world continues to inspire me daily.

PARENTS AND CAREGIVERS

To all parents and caregivers of children with special needs. You take on more than most, and continuously strive to better the future of your children, often without the support you and your children need. I hope this book eases your challenging journey and offers you a useful tool for incorporating helpful exercises in your home. Remember, you are not alone!

TEACHERS

You are one of our children's primary influencers and game changers. Helping you to create a safe and effective classroom for all children is my main goal. Outside of the home, you have the most impact on our children's development.

FELLOW SERVICE PROVIDERS

Lastly, to my fellow occupational therapists and service providers, you work hard to meet the needs of your clients, often not seeing the fruits of your labor. Working alongside you has been a great privilege and is what pushes me to continue finding effective solutions to our client's and their family's needs every day. Together we can make a difference!

FREE GIFT

Thank you for purchasing our book

As a special thank you, we'd love to gift you with FREE companion resources to help you on your journey!

DOWNLOAD NOW

RITP.INFO/TLR-BOOK

Transform your Treatment Plans ANYWHERE, ANYTIME!

Access to 100+ exercises to address retained reflexes

Collect exercises together into easy to access playlists

Share playlists with other app users!

Kid friendly easy-to-follow videos and instructions right in your pocket!

Access to exclusive learning videos by Kokeb Mcdonald, OTR/L & Author

DOWNLOAD OUR APP NOW

RITP.INFO/APP

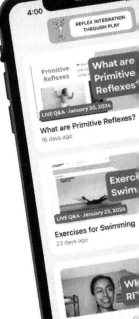

LEARN MORE
RITP.INFO/CERTIFICATION

Are you a Service Provider ready to grow?

Explore our Reflex Integration Through Play™ Certification Program!

 ## Say Hello to...

- Refining and expanding your clinical skills to effectively address the most complex developmental delays
- Broadening your professional and business opportunities available to you as a therapist
- Having a done-for-you treatment and at-home plan highly targeted to treat children with developmental delays

The Program Includes

In-Depth Courses & Training
Live Support Calls
Collaborative Community
Access to Mobile App
Done-For-You Treatment Plans
Step-by-Step
Play-Based Exercises

American Occupational Therapy Association

Approved Provider

LEARN MORE

RITP.INFO/FAMILY

Skyrocket your Child's Progress at HOME!

As a parent, do you...

- See developmental challenges in your child and don't know where to start?
- Want to accelerate your child's therapy program?
- Feel overwhelmed with at-home movement plans and want to make it more fun?

We want to support you with our Reflex Integration Through Play™ Family Bundle!

Our Family Bundle Includes:

Hours of training on play-based reflex integration tailored to a home environment

In-depth on-demand course covering retained reflexes & their impact on your child

Access to our Mobile App (100+ exercise instructions!)

Access to a private membership community

Bring Reflex Integration Through Play™ to Your School!

Are you an educator looking to provide fun movement breaks & sensory diet programs for your students?

Your Students Will...

- Grow in their energy levels
- Improve their attention span and academic performance
- Progress in their social skills and physical abilities

LEARN MORE

RITP.INFO/SCHOOL

TABLE OF CONTENTS

PREFACE

Welcome to *An Interactive Guide to* Tonic Labyrinthine Reflex (TLR), the fourth book in the series *Integrating Primitive Reflexes Through Play and Exercise*. I hope you'll find these exercises simple, fun and useful.

If this is your first experience with this series, please also check out the **first three books in the series on the Moro Reflex, Asymmetrical Tonic Neck Reflex (ATNR) and Symmetrical Tonic Neck Reflex (STNR).** Much of the information in this book, such as the introduction, reflex descriptions and definitions, is similar to that in the previous books. Working first on the Moro Reflex, and alongside the ATNR and STNR, may also be essential to success with the exercises for Tonic Labyrinthine Reflex (TLR) included in this book. If you have read the other books, understand primitive reflexes and their benefits, and simply want to focus on the TLR, you can skip to Chapter 2, and begin the program.

Many parents spend time reading about research and findings but are left more confused and overwhelmed than they were before, as much of the information available is geared toward professionals. What most parents need is a practical guide that relies on research yet is written in terms they can understand and easily put to use. After publishing the first book in this series on the Moro Reflex, and later on the ATNR and STNR, I received positive feedback from several parents, teachers and service providers who said that the simple, step-by-step instructions were helping them. They also reported that they had been looking for a simple guide with clear instructions but, until now, had not been able to find one. If you are one of these parents, you know what it feels like to balance your work, life, parental duties, and still make sure you are providing the best possible support for your child's developmental needs. This book is mainly for you.

The books in this series are not presented in any specific order. If you choose, you can work on many reflexes at the same time or in any sequence. However, if you suspect your child may have Moro Reflex retention, for example, I highly recommend you start with that reflex. Since the Moro Reflex affects all of our senses, including our fight and flight response, it is best to start calming the nervous system before tackling the challenge of integrating other reflexes, which can be stressful; however, you do not need to have the Moro Reflex fully integrated to begin working on other reflexes.

While you may begin working on any reflex—or multiple reflexes—as you first utilize this series, it is essential that you know the retention of one reflex often leads to the retention of another reflex. It is not always clear, however, which reflex is dominating the body at a given time. **To be safe, I recommend screening for and working on *all* primitive reflexes with a trained specialist.** With the results of comprehensive screening, you will be better informed and able to implement these guidebooks for optimal results. In the meantime, you can safely incorporate these fun games and exercises into your clinic, classroom or home routine in a way that makes sense for you and your client, and observe your client's performance. I chose these specific exercises because they are easy to implement and allow for easy observation of the retained reflex pattern when it is present in the body. Plus, they are fun, and parents can participate in at-home exercises, allowing for healthy play. A win-win for all!

I hope you'll find the information and exercises in this book helpful on your journey to support the development of the clients with whom you work. I also invite you to join our growing community on our Facebook page at https://www.facebook.com/integratingreflexes. There you'll find discussions and further information about our reflex book series.

Kokeb Girma McDonald, OTR/L
California, 2022

INTRODUCTION

A child's treatment program should be a collaboration between parents and therapists. Therapists can guide a child's development better if they partner with the parents in the treatment plan. The best intervention is one that carries over into the home. A weekly therapy session without the parents' collaboration and education will not be as effective on a child's development. It is a team approach, like rowing a canoe; you will get to your destination faster and with less energy expenditure when everyone on the boat works together.

Since parents are their child's first teachers, and are the most likely to motivate and influence them, they can incorporate the therapist's recommendations throughout the day. By doing that, they can (1) provide needed repetition and (2) easily discern what interventions are working well and give feedback to the therapist. This process not only helps to achieve faster results but also reduces the number of therapy sessions needed and the total cost. However, when parent-therapist collaboration is weak, the therapist can only rely on data collected during an individual session in a controlled environment, instead of having a better understanding of the child's development and skills that were carried over to the child's natural settings. This lack of data can lead to termination of a potentially effective intervention and a waste of time, energy and money. Children need a lot of repetition; if the child does not have enough carryover, there will be inconsistency, confusion, lack of interest and frustration.

As a working parent, I can testify that it is hard to come home from a busy work day and still manage to do therapeutic exercises with your child. You are tired, and your child is tired. The last thing you probably want to do is start an activity your child is going to fight you over. Even as a trained and experienced pediatric occupational therapist, I am challenged when I make these home exercises a chore for my child and less motivated when I do not fully understand the reason behind the activities. Children learn through play. What my child wants is to spend time with me and play. It takes creativity and guidance to set up a home program that can be easily carried over to the house. The best ones are those that are fun, explorative and playful for the child and you.

In this book, I will provide simple, play-based and step-by-step therapeutic exercises that are focused on the Tonic Labyrinthine Reflex (TLR). This book is different from the others since it contains advanced exercises that can be done with adults as well as children.

Primitive reflexes are involuntary movement patterns that are present at birth and should have been integrated before the child reaches 12 months. When these reflexes do not stay dormant, they will begin to affect the way the child processes the environment and responds to it. We usually can see these responses by the way the child reacts emotionally (behavior) and moves (physically). The best way to integrate these reflexes is by recreating infantile activities the child should have done to integrate the system in the first place. These exercises give the child a second chance to reintegrate and rewire the brain-body connection.

The goal of this handbook is to try and meet the following needs:

1. Provide resources for new occupational therapists on the first primitive reflex, the Tonic Labyrinthine Reflex (TLR). This handbook has some basic therapeutic exercises that help integrate the TLR. It helps the reader know symptoms and behaviors that retained TLR accompanies.

2. Create clear, step-by-step exercises. It is beneficial and necessary to know why we chose a specific activity. In this book, you will find a menu of therapeutic exercises that challenge or help integrate the TLR. The level of difficulty at the beginning and gradual improvement can, later on, help you adjust your treatment sessions.

3. Caregivers' training and involvement: The best intervention is one that carries over into the home. By having an exercise that can quickly be done at home, you can provide education and

needed repetition. This, in turn, will create faster results. Parents and service providers can follow their communication and weekly activities by using tracking charts provided in the appendix of this book.

This program is not intended as medical advice and should be done with the help of a trained service provider.

This book should not be used to diagnose or replace other therapeutic reflex integration programs.

CHAPTER 1

PRIMITIVE REFLEXES AND THEIR BENEFITS

THE BENEFITS OF REFLEXES

Primitive reflexes are involuntary movement patterns controlled by the brain stem and are executed without reaching the cortical or conscious part of the brain. All primitive reflexes emerge in utero, are present at birth, and should be integrated between 6 – 12 months after birth. Seven primitive reflexes emerge in utero and integrate before the child reaches about 12 months of age. These reflexes are Moro Reflex, Palmar Reflex, Asymmetrical Tonic Neck Reflex, Rooting Reflex, Spinal Galant Reflex, Tonic Labyrinthine Reflex and Symmetrical Tonic Neck Reflex.

These primary reflexes are all necessary for the infant's first-year survival and during its transition to the world. Together they help the infant go through the birth canal, take its first breath, withdraw from hazardous stimuli, urinate, creep, grasp, lift its head, open its mouth, suck and swallow, and kick. All these movements are involuntary, and the infant cannot control or know what it is doing. Each primitive reflex has its own benefit, and is a building block to the infant's future movements and how it perceives the world via its senses. When the infant is in utero and after birth, it does not know what it needs or how to get it, it just has primitive reflexes. Instinctively the infant responds to the world via these primitive reflexes.

As the infant grows, a healthy and typically developing brain allows the infant to benefit from these primitive reflexes, and gradually begins to integrate the reflexes to develop voluntary and purposeful movements. If there are any pregnancy and/or birthing complications, genetic abnormality or injuries to the brain, or incorrect functioning, primitive reflexes may stay active in the body. If primitive reflexes remain active, there will always be involuntary movements or responses present in the body. These reflexive responses will appear in the patterns in which the child moves, behaves or reacts to stimuli. Moreover, as the child continues to grow, he or she may begin to perceive the world in an immature way, and behavioral challenges may follow when primitive reflexes are actively present.

Primitive Reflexes are succeeded by Postural Reflexes, and their retention will affect a child's development. It will be challenging to work on a child's Postural Reflexes, for instance, without first going back and making sure the brain has integrated the Primitive Reflexes. When a child's brain is healthy and developing normally, maturity and growth become automatic. The child goes through movement patterns that are considered natural and instinctive while assisting the brain in integrating Primitive Reflexes. We usually see a disturbance in the brain when the child either does not go through the milestones or skips them all together. For example, a child moves from sitting to walking, skipping the crawling phase, which is essential. In fact, every stage is essential, and the best way we can integrate these reflexes is by following the natural process, which is mimicking activities and movements that are missed or done incorrectly in early stages, and letting the brain experience it so it can rewire itself.

CHAPTER 2

WHAT IS THE TONIC LABYRINTHINE REFLEX (TLR)?

A. ONSET AND PATTERNS OF THE TONIC LABYRINTHINE REFLEX (TLR)

The Tonic Labyrinthine Reflex (TLR) is a reflex pattern that is present at birth and activated by the movement of the head's position. TLR is an involuntary reaction in response to the head flexion and extension position with respect to the spine. When the head is in front of the spine (flexed), the rest of the body responds in a flexed position in unison. Similarly, when the head is behind the spine (extends), the rest of the body responds in an extended position.

To break down the reflex's name, the word Tonic means tone and Labyrinthine stands for Labrinth, the two inner ears located inside the head, containing the vestibule, cochlea and semicircular canals. In short, the TLR influences head control, alignment, muscle tone, and balance against gravity.

The TLR has two positions, TLR forward and TLR backward, as in Image #1. The TLR forward is the same position that the fetus holds in the womb. It emerges in utero, is present at birth, and integrates around four months of age after birth. The TLR backward emerges in utero, is present at birth, and starts to slowly integrate at six weeks after birth up to 3 years of age.

The TLR helps differentiate and coordinate the front and back of the body. It "splits" the body in the frontal plane (front and back or posterior and anterior) and enables the flexion and extension of muscles in response to head position. The coordination of these two positions helps the brain and body to coordinate the flexion and extension muscle movements, muscle tone, upright posture, front-back coordination, head-righting skills, vestibular skills, proprioception, and spatial body awareness. Other reflexes, such as the Symmetrical Tonic Neck Reflex, "split" the body horizontally (top and bottom), while the Asymmetrical Tonic Neck Reflex (ATNR) "splits" the body vertically (left and right). For more information on the STNR and ATNR, please refer to Books #2 and #3 in this series by visiting www.amazon.com/dp/B08R1ZLGYQ.

Position 1: TLR Forward   **Position 2: TLR Backward**

Image #1: Tonic Labyrinthine Reflex (TLR) Pattern

POSITION 1: TLR FORWARD

Sensory trigger: Head moving in front of the spine

Motor responses include:

- Flexion of the upper body

- Flexion of the lower body

- Flexion of the core muscles

Image #2: TLR forward causing the body to go into full flexion

POSITION 2: TLR BACKWARD

Sensory trigger: Head moving to the back of the spine

Motor responses include:

- Extension of the upper body

- Extension of the lower body

- Extension of the back

Image #3: TLR backward causing the body to go into full extension

B. BENEFITS OF THE TONIC LABYRINTHINE REFLEX (TLR)

HEAD CONTROL

One of the earliest and most crucial skills infants learn is head control. Head control is key to gaining proper balance, sense of body awareness, alignment, posture and coordination. At the beginning of an infant's life, the head is heavy and difficult to move against gravity. However, as the infant develops and grows, he/she will begin to move the head against gravity and go through developmental milestones such as rolling, lifting the head off the ground, sitting, crawling, standing, walking and running. The TLR is one of the critical primitive reflexes that influences these milestones.

ROLLING

Rolling is one of the milestones babies start to practice as early as 3 to 4 months of age. The beginning phase for rolling can be seen when the baby starts to lift its head and shoulders off the floor during tummy time and rocks from side to side. Or, when placed on their back, they lift their legs off the floor and rock from side to side, initiating segmental rolling either from the upper or lower body. These repetitive movements help develop muscle tone and coordination, and prepare the baby for rolling, creeping, standing and walking.

VESTIBULAR SKILLS

The **Vestibular System** is a sensory organ, located in both inner ears (see Image #4 below), and gives feedback to the brain regarding the head position, motion, balance, posture and spatial relation. Similar to the visual and auditory systems, any reflex pattern that moves the head, including the Tonic Labyrinthine Reflex, helps develop the Vestibular System.

Image #4: Location of the vestibular system

Auditory figure-ground is the ability to hear specific sounds in a noisy environment. For example: a child will be able to respond to your call amid all the noise at the playground or while watching TV. **Auditory localization** is the ability to perceive and locate from where a sound is coming. For example: a child can turn toward the sound and locate the source.

Image #5: Head turns toward a source of sound

Binaural hearing is the ability to hear with both ears equally, and **receptive language** refers to the ability to understand and interpret sounds, words and sentences accurately. For a more in-depth understanding, screening, and treatment options for receptive language and speech, please refer to a speech therapist.

VISUAL SKILLS

Any reflex pattern that moves the head, including the TLR, affects and influences visual skills development. In this book, we will focus on visual skills the TLR partially influences. If vision skills are an area of concern, consider working on additional reflexes, such as the Moro Reflex, Asymmetrical Tonic Neck Reflex (ATNR), Symmetrical Tonic Neck Reflex (STNR) and Spinal Galant Reflex (definitions of these reflexes are in the end Glossary). For a more in-depth understanding, screening, and treatment options on visual skills and perception, please refer to a trained vision therapist.

The **visual perceptual skill** is the brain's ability to understand what the eyes see and interpret it appropriately, including depth, figure-ground (distinguishing objects from the background), location, visual closure (recognizing a familiar object when it is partially obscured), and more.

Visual acuity is the eye's ability to see clearly. Note that a person can have high visual acuity (i.e., 20/20 vision) and still have difficulty with visual perception.

Visual fixation is the eye's ability to maintain gaze on an object for an extended period of time. Visual fixation is the first critical skill to develop before more advanced visual skills. Once the eyes can fixate, they can learn to track a moving target. There are two visual tracking skills: saccade and smooth pursuit.

Near-to-far and far-to-near visual tracking are the eyes' ability to move in opposite directions to track an object. When both eyes focus on a near object, they have to converge (move inward, towards each other), and when both eyes focus on a far object, they have to diverge (move outward, away from each other). Therefore, fluid visual tracking requires coordinating both eye muscles to work together and in the opposite direction (convergence and divergence). During the TLR integration, when a child lifts the head off the floor, and begins to roll, sit, stand, and walk, these skills continue to develop.

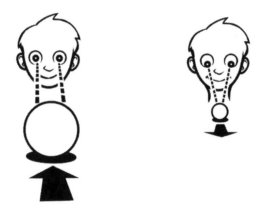

Image #6: Visual Fixation and Near & Far Visual Tracking

Peripheral vision: is the eyes' ability to use side vision while gazing straight ahead. The TLR influences this skill.

Binocular vision is the ability to move and use both eyes equally and effectively. When binocular vision is poor, it can cause disorders such as amblyopia (also known as "lazy eye" with one eye having less acuity) and strabismus (crossed or misaligned eyes).

There are two visual tracking skills: saccade and smooth pursuit. **Saccade** is the eye's ability to accurately jump back and forth between targets. **Smooth pursuit** is the eye's ability to smoothly and accurately track a moving object or line. For instance, while copying from a whiteboard, the eyes need to follow a straight line (*smooth pursuit*) to read what is on the board and look down quickly from the board to the paper without losing their place (*saccade*). Similarly, when we read our eyes follow a straight line (*smooth pursuit*) from left to right, then quickly down to the second line of the first letter on the left side (*saccade*).

MUSCLE TONE

Muscle tone is the resistance of a muscle to active or passive stretch or the overall tension of the muscle. Muscle tone has three main functions:

1. Assists in maintaining posture.

2. Stores up energy and releases the stored energy during movements.

3. Displays a "spring" like property to dampen jerky movements, and produce a smooth and coordinated action.

POSTURE

Posture is how we align and hold our spine with our shoulders, head, pelvis, hips and feet. There are two types of postures: dynamic and static. **Dynamic posture** is how the body is aligned while in motion (e.g., walking, running, swimming, etc.). **Static posture** is how the body is aligned when there is no motion (e.g., sitting, standing, sleeping). The TLR is one of the primitive reflexes that directly influences both dynamic and static postures.

The TLR influences the whole body flexion and extension, separation of the front and back of the body, muscle tone, head-righting skills and upright posture. To have an upright posture, both agonist and antagonist muscles have to work in unison to keep the head and body up. When the TLR is not fully developed or integrated, muscle tone and posture will be affected, and holding the head in a neutral spine position will be difficult. (See Image #7 below.)

Image #7: Standing posture affected by TLR forward:
the head forward causes slouching and forward flexion of the
body as compared to when the head is aligned with the spine

AN OVERVIEW OF THE BENEFITS OF THE TONIC LABYRINTHINE REFLEX (TLR):

- Assists with the birthing process

- Assists with cross-lateral movements in early development, such as rolling, crawling, sitting, kneeling, standing and walking

- Assists with head-righting, specifically with flexion and extension

- Influences muscle tone, neck control and core stability developments

- Assists with changes in position (gravitational pull) by helping the body balance and create stability

- Influences muscle-ligaments and tension between the front and back of the body

- Contributes to whole body movement coordination

- Assists with proper space orientation, sense of direction, distance from self, velocity

- Contributes to the coordination of opposing muscles (i.e, agonist and antagonist muscles)

- Contributes to the organization and perception of binocular vision (the ability to see with both eyes equally)

- Supports binaural hearing (the ability to hear with both ears equally)

- Assists with near-to-far and far-to-near visual tracking (i.e., convergence and divergence)

- Influences the auditory processing system (hearing)

- Influences the vestibular system, which affects balance, spatial orientation and posture

- Assists with fine motor skills and eye-hand coordination

- Assists with speech and language development

- Influences the learning process and skills

- Influences static and dynamic postures

- Influences gross motor coordination

C. RETAINED TONIC LABYRINTHINE REFLEX (TLR): SIGNS, SYMPTOMS AND BEHAVIORS

When the TLR is active (retained) in the body past the integration stage, it creates delays in a child's fine motor and gross motor skills, auditory processing, visual processing, vestibular skills, proprioception, and focus and attention skills.

SIGNS AND SYMPTOMS OF A RETAINED TONIC LABYRINTHINE REFLEX (TLR)

GROSS AND FINE MOTOR DEVELOPMENT CHALLENGES:

- Dislikes physical activity

- Poor balance

- Poor motor planning and coordination

- Poor muscle tone; fatigues easily when lifting arms overhead

- Poor seated posture; prefers to lean on or rest head on arm

- Poor head control

- Poor balance when looking up or down; walking up/down stairs can be difficult

- May have difficulty with cross-lateral skills causing coordination problems; may have stiff and jerky movements

- May exhibit <u>mixed dominance</u>; interchanges use of left and right hand, foot, eye, ear for same tasks

- Fatigues easily; lifting arms (e.g., writing) is exhausting

- Poor alignment skills; finds working with math columns difficult

- Dyspraxia tendencies

Image #8: A child rests its head on an arm to compensate for lack of head control.

POSTURE AND STABILITY CHALLENGES:

- Tense muscles, stiffness, rigidity and hypertonic (influence of TLR backwards)

- Weak muscle tone; slouched, stooped posture and hypotonic (influence of TLR forward)

- Poor muscle tone and overall posture

- Slouching seated or standing posture

- Preference for toe walking

- Head appears heavy; tilts head to front or back

- Poor standing posture (e.g., chin forward, body flexed, shoulders raised, slouched back, etc.)

- Poor standing posture (e.g., head slightly extended, toe walking, back extended, etc.)

- Poor seated posture; will rest head on desk because head feels heavy; wraps legs around chair legs, etc.

Image #9: Example of static posture (i.e., seated) with retained TLR

VISUAL SKILLS CHALLENGES:

- Poor spatial awareness (e.g., disorganized, forgetful, losing track of time, etc.)

- Difficulty with visual motor skills

- Bumps into things and people when moving around

- Poor visual perception (e.g., words appear to run together with no spaces in between; letter reversals, etc.)

- Poor spatial perception (e.g., difficulty judging space, direction, distance)

- Difficulty reading (e.g., takes longer; poor comprehension; frustration and avoidance of reading)

- Poor eye movement (e.g., difficulty with near-to-far and far-to-near vision)

- Difficulty with math and working with math columns

- May experience motion sickness; vertigo

- Fear of heights

AUDITORY SKILLS CHALLENGES:

- Difficulty with speech and articulation

- Poor auditory processing (e.g., challenges with multiple instructions and verbal learning)

- Poor sequencing skills, which effects speech, spelling and composition

- Difficulty with spelling and composition

- Difficulty following multiple instructions; struggles with verbal learning

ATTENTION AND CONCENTRATION CHALLENGES:

- Difficulty holding still and concentrating

- Difficulty paying attention when head is down (e.g., at a desk or reading)

- May appear disconnected to feelings

- Frustration; low self esteem; lack of interest in school

- Difficulty understanding cause and effect (e.g., may make the same mistakes repeatedly)

- Disorganized and forgetful

- Loses track of time that results in incomplete, missing or late assignments

CHAPTER 3

TESTING AND SCREENING FOR TLR

There are specific testing methods that trained therapists and service providers use to check for a retained Tonic Labyrinthine Reflex (TLR). This book, however, is not designed to teach any one testing method. This screening list should only be used to gather data, not to determine a specific diagnosis. In addition, while not a formal evaluation method, I have compiled a symptoms and behavioral checklist (Table #1) to be filled out by parents and service providers during the screening process.

A. SYMPTOMS AND BEHAVIORAL CHECKLIST: TONIC LABYRINTHINE REFLEX (TLR)

Observe the child and circle the number that best represents the severity of the symptoms you observe. You can use this checklist first to gather data for an initial baseline and then again 6–12 weeks after the start of intervention to assess progress.

TESTING AND SCREENING FOR TONIC LABYRINTHINE REFLEX (TLR)

	Symptoms and Behaviors						
1	Poor muscle tone and overall posture (e.g., stooped posture, slouched, and hypotonicity)	0	1	2	3	4	5
2	Poor muscle tone; fatigues easily when lifting arms overhead	0	1	2	3	4	5
3	Difficulty copying from a board; loses place, skips lines, or becomes confused	0	1	2	3	4	5
4	Poor seated posture, prefers to lean or rest head on arms, wraps legs around chair legs, slouches, etc.	0	1	2	3	4	5
5	Poor auditory processing (e.g., challenges with multiple instructions and verbal learning)	0	1	2	3	4	5
6	Difficulty reading (e.g., takes longer; poor comprehension; frustration and avoidance of reading)	0	1	2	3	4	5
7	Poor standing posture (e.g., slouches, chin sticks out, body flexed, shoulders raised)	0	1	2	3	4	5
8	Fear of heights (e.g., afraid to climb up and down stairs or play structure)	0	1	2	3	4	5
9	Difficulty with ball games (e.g., catching, throwing, kicking and hitting, etc.)	0	1	2	3	4	5
10	Poor seated posture on floor (e.g., slouches or W sits)	0	1	2	3	4	5

11	Difficulty with near-to-far and far-to-near visual tracking (poor eye movements)	0	1	2	3	4	5
12	May have stiff and jerky movements, tense muscles, rigidity, and hypertonicity.	0	1	2	3	4	5
13	Poor (weak) core muscle stability and balance	0	1	2	3	4	5
14	Poor head control (e.g. head appears heavy, tilts forward or back, difficulty lifting head off the floor, "wobbly head")	0	1	2	3	4	5
15	Loses track of time (e.g., late work, incomplete, missing, etc.)	0	1	2	3	4	5
16	Poor balance and stability	0	1	2	3	4	5
17	Poor walking posture; may prefer to toe walk, head slightly extended or leaning forward, and body somewhat stiff.	0	1	2	3	4	5
18	Difficulty recognizing social cues (e.g., may appear disconnected to feelings)	0	1	2	3	4	5
19	Difficulty with speech and articulation	0	1	2	3	4	5
20	Difficulty holding still, concentration and attention (e.g., may have ADD or ADHD tendencies)	0	1	2	3	4	5
21	Poor spatial awareness (e.g., disorganized, forgetful, losing track of time, etc.)	0	1	2	3	4	5
22	Difficulty with multiple-step movement instructions and activities (e.g., skipping, jumping and balancing games, etc.)	0	1	2	3	4	5

23	Slower working speed (e.g., fatigues easily and functions slower than most)	0	1	2	3	4	5
24	Difficulty and frustration playing sports	0	1	2	3	4	5
25	May exhibit mixed dominance: interchanges use of left and right (e.g., during handwriting, throwing, kicking, etc.)	0	1	2	3	4	5
26	Poor visual alignment skills; makes working with math columns difficult (vertical visual tracking)	0	1	2	3	4	5
27	Poor spatial perception (e.g., difficulty judging space, direction, distance; may bump into things and people)	0	1	2	3	4	5
28	Tendency to be disorganized and forgetful	0	1	2	3	4	5
29	Difficulty understanding cause and effect (e.g., may make the same mistakes repeatedly)	0	1	2	3	4	5
30	Difficulty paying attention when head is down (e.g., at a desk or reading)	0	1	2	3	4	5

Table #1: Symptoms and Behavior Checklist for Tonic Labyrinthine Reflex (TLR)

Note: Usually, one retained reflex leads to the retention of other reflexes. To be safe, work on all of the primitive reflexes. Before working with a child, go through the symptoms checklist, and rate the severity of the symptoms or behaviors on a scale of 0–5, 0 being "not seen" to 5, being "seen all the time."

You can use the following exercises as part of the screening process **to determine if further testing is needed.** Inability to perform the following exercises well might be a sign of a retained TLR.

Note: Some of the screening can be difficult, and is best used with older kids and adults. In addition to your clinical observation, if you are working with an older client or adult, have them be part of the observation process. It is important that they are aware of their body and note any changes they might feel, including emotional state, and report back to you.

B. SCREEN 1: HEAD PENDULUM STANDING

MATERIALS: None

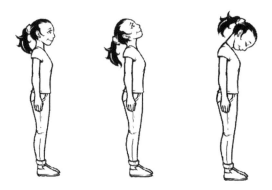

1. Have the client stand with both feet flat on the floor.

2. Ask clients to raise their head and look up for 5–7 seconds while maintaining balance.

3. Observation:

    When the head **looks up (extension)**, the body might:

    *   Jerk backwards

    *   Extend the back

    *   Stiffen

    *   Extend arms, hands and legs

Note: These movements can be slight, so make sure to observe carefully.

---

4. Go back to starting position.

5. Ask client to look down on the floor for 5–7 seconds while maintaining balance.

6. Observation:

When the head **looks down (flexion)**, the body might:

- Flex forward

- Collapse forward

- Lose balance; fall forward

- Flex arms, hands and legs

Note: These movements can be slight, so make sure to observe carefully.

EYES CLOSED

- After the client is able to lift their head up and down, and adequately maintain balance, you can further test their balance by repeating the activity **with eyes closed.**

OBSERVATIONS

- Can they maintain balance while moving the head up and down?

- Can their head move independent of the rest of the body?

- Are they relaxed and maintaining steady breathing?

- Are there any parts of the body flexing and extending?

- Were there shoulder movements and tension?

SIGNS OF TLR RETENTION

- Loss of balance and falling

- Disorientation; fear of falling

- Anxiousness and sweating

- Nausea

- Unable to look up and maintain head extension

When the head **looks up (extension)**, the body might:

- Jerk backwards

- Extend the back

- Stiffen

- Extend arms, hands and legs

When the head **looks down (flexion)**, the body might:

- Flex forward

- Collapse forward

- Lose balance; fall forward

- Flex arms, hands and legs

Note: These movements can be slight, so make sure to observe carefully.

Signs the TLR is integrated well:

- Able to maintain balance and stability

- Able to move head with ease, independent of the rest of the body

- Shoulders, neck and face stay relaxed

- Breathing is relaxed (no tension)

C. SCREEN 2: HEAD PENDULUM WITH STRAIGHT ARMS

MATERIALS: None

OPTION 1: ARMS SHOULDER HEIGHT (IN FRONT)

1. Have the client stand with both feet flat on the floor and both arms straight, in front at shoulder height.

2. Ask clients to extend their head to look up and hold for 5–7 seconds while maintaining balance.

3. Observation:

   When the head **looks up (extension)**, the body might:

   - Jerk backwards

- Extend the back

- Stiffen

- Extend arms, hands and legs

- Extend arms up with the head

- Have arms that fatigue quickly and change positions

Note: These movements can be slight, so make sure to observe carefully.

4. Go back to starting position.

5. Ask clients to flex their head to look down on their feet for another 5–7 seconds.

6. Observation:

When the head **looks down (flexion)**, the body might:

- Flex forward

- Collapse forward

- Lose balance; fall forward

- Flex arms, hips, and legs

- Flex arms up with the head

- Have arms that fatigue quickly; have difficulty keeping arms parallel to the floor

Note: These movements can be slight, so make sure to observe carefully.

OPTION 2: ARMS OVERHEAD (STRAIGHT UP)

1. Have the client stand with both feet flat on the floor and both arms straight, over their ears.

2. Ask clients to extend their head to look up and hold for 5–7 seconds.

3. Observation:

    When the head **looks up (extension)**, the body might:

    *   Jerk backwards

    *   Extend the back or leans back

    *   Stiffen

    *   Extend arms, hands and legs

    *   Extend arms further with the head

> **Note:** These movements can be slight, so make sure to observe carefully.

4. Go back to starting position.

5. Ask clients to flex their head to look down on their feet for another 5–7 seconds.

6. Observation:

   When the head **looks down (flexion)**, the body might:

   - Flex forward

   - Collapse forward

   - Lose balance; fall forward

   - Flex arms, hips and legs

   - Begin to drop arms down

   - Have arms that fatigue quickly; have difficulty keeping arms straight over the head

---

Note: These movements can be slight, so make sure to observe carefully.

OBSERVATIONS

- Can they maintain balance and ease of movement?

- Can their head move independent of the rest of the body?

- Are they relaxed and maintaining steady breathing?

- Are there any parts of the body flexing and extending with head movement?

- Are they unable to keep arms straight?

- Can they maintain muscle tone and strength?

- Are they fatigued easily?

SIGNS OF TLR RETENTION

- Loss of balance and falling

- Disorientation; fear of falling

- Anxiousness and sweating

- Nausea

- Unable to look up and maintain head extension

CHAPTER 4

ADDRESSING A RETAINED TONIC LABYRINTHINE REFLEX (TLR)

A. INTERVENTION AND TREATMENT PLANNING

A number of interventions may be appropriate for those with a retained TLR. One of the simplest ways to help integrate primitive reflexes is by mimicking early-childhood movement patterns. In addition, we can incorporate exercises to target muscles that contribute to the specific reflex pattern.

Together, the TLR forward and backward help differentiate and coordinate the front and back of the body. TLR "splits" the body in the frontal plane (front and back or posterior and anterior) and enables the flexion and extension of skeletal muscles in response to head position. The coordination of these two antagonistic skeletal muscle groups helps the body move smoothly, develop muscle tone, and maintain an upright posture, head control and balance. The exercises in this book focus on these antagonistic muscles (whole-body flexion and extension) that the TLR directly influences.

The exercises compiled in this book are for those receiving occupational therapy and other reflex integration treatments. In the back of the book, I have added advanced exercises, preferably best used by a skilled Pilates Instructor. If you are not a trained specialist, please consult with one. The exercises can be used in clinics, schools, homes and gyms. Once you have introduced the activities, you can use them as a daily home program to be followed by caregivers and clients, and as a movement break in a school setting with the help of a trained professional.

The age groups with which you can use these exercises vary from preschoolers to adults. You do not need to do every exercise listed in this book since it is not appropriate for everyone. Please use your clinical judgment, client history, and the level of support clients require before you introduce an activity. The exercises give the reader an overall understanding of TLR movement patterns and the types of exercises challenging for those with retained TLR.

It is challenging to trigger only one reflex when using a play-and-exercise approach to treatment. Therefore, as a clinician, you must know the other reflex patterns, and whether they are triggered and affect the client's performance. **To best serve the client, try the exercises from simple to hard before adding more challenging tasks that might frustrate them.**

Note: A correct visual processing skill is necessary for learning. It is crucial that a trained practitioner screens a child to rule out possible retained reflexes and visual skill delays that may affect learning.

To help incorporate auditory processing skills and responses, we will use cues, such as clapping, snapping, counting, or the use of a metronome. A **metronome** is a device used by musicians that marks a tempo in beats-per-minute. You can use a physical metronome device or download a mobile app. The use of a metronome will increase the challenge of the exercise and, at the same time, help you focus more on the child and less on giving verbal cues. When choosing a tempo, if the child tends to go very fast, start with a faster tempo, and gradually slow it down. If the child tends to go very slowly, start with a slower tempo, and gradually increase the speed. Do not get frustrated. Meet children at their skill level.

B. ACCOMMODATIONS

A child with a retained TLR may have delayed motor coordination skills, visual perception, postural control, attention and concentration. For a classroom or workstation, choose one or more of the following accommodations to meet the child's needs:

1. Place materials to copy on the child's desk to minimize head movement during copying.

2. Allow working in different positions. Do not focus on the upright seated position when you are focusing on education. Allow the child to be comfortable and not expend a lot of energy to maintain postural balance. Instead, provide a variety of options, such as:

    a. Standing at a desk to write.

    b. Laying down on the floor to read.

    c. Using a wedge to lift hips more than 90 degrees while seated.

    d. Using a slanted board to elevate working materials and keep the head straighter.

3. Break down verbal instruction:

    a. Provide written instruction for review.

    b. Have the child repeat the first instruction before adding additional instructions.

4. For movement activities, accommodate right- and left-side confusion by providing the following:

   a. Visual cues to help differentiate the right and left sides of the body.

   b. A picture or video to imitate.

   c. A breakdown of the steps.

5. Provide movement breaks from the exercises described in this book to help promote TLR integration.

6. Do not force games and sports; the child may not be ready for advanced movements without breaking down the steps.

7. If reading is difficult, try the following strategies:

   a. Have the child track letters with fingers.

   b. Use a ruler or visual cues under the line the child is reading.

   c. Cover all text except the line being read.

C. EXERCISES TO PROMOTE TONIC LABYRINTHINE REFLEX (TLR)

The exercises below can be used in the order you think is best for your client. Follow the order presented here or combine the exercises with others during your session. The manner in which you utilize the exercises depends on the environment, the client's state, and the materials you have on hand. For example, make the activities fun and exciting when working with younger children, but feel free to create more of a workout session with older children and adults. Avoid activities that create frustration and anxiety. As much as possible, try to make the exercises fun and enjoyable. For kids who are younger and refuse to cooperate, incorporate the use of positive reinforcement or rewards to encourage participation.

> **Note:** The following exercises challenge more than one of the primitive reflexes, including the TLR, encourage bilateral coordination, balance, spatial awareness, visual skills, auditory and motor planning skills. Use the additional modifications and accommodations for exercises that many find difficult.

1) HEAD PENDULUM STANDING

MATERIALS: None

1. Have the client stand with both feet flat on the floor.

2. Ask client to raise head and look up for 5–7 seconds.

3. Go back to starting position.

4. Ask client to look down on the floor for another 5–7 seconds.

5. Repeat 3–5 times.

GOALS

1. Complete smooth and controlled movement, independently

2. Balance and control

3. Differentiation between the upper body and lower body

4. Differentiation of the head from the rest of the body

5. Differentiation between the front and back of the body

POSITIVE SIGNS

- ☐ Able to maintain balance

- ☐ Able to move head with ease, independent of the rest of the body

- ☐ Relaxed shoulders, neck and face

- ☐ Feet stay flat on the floor

NEGATIVE SIGNS

- ☐ Loss of balance and falling

- ☐ Disorientation; fear of falling; maybe even nauseousness

- ☐ Anxiousness and sweat

- ☐ Unable to look up and maintain head extension

When the **head looks up**, the body might:

- Jerk backward

- Extend

- Stiffen

- Extend arms, hands and legs

When the **head looks down**, the body might:

- Flex forward

- Collapse

- Fall forward

- Flex arms, hands and legs

VARIATION

ADVANCED

By closing the eyes and adding uneven surfaces you will challenge balance more.

1. Do the exercise with eyes closed.

2. Do the exercise on an uneven surface (e.g., a balance board).

2) WHOLE BODY PENDULUM

MATERIALS: None

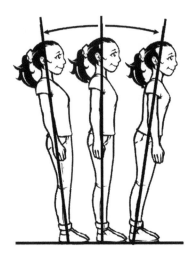

1. Have the client stand with both feet flat on the floor.

2. Ask the client to lean forward, with straight spine and head, and hold for 1–3 seconds.

3. Go back to starting position.

4. Ask the client to lean back, with straight spine and head, and hold for 1–3 seconds.

5. Repeat 1–3 times.

GOALS

1. Complete smooth and controlled movement, independently

2. Balance and control

3. Differentiation between the upper and lower body

4. Differentiation of the head from the rest of the body

5. Able to bring the body straight forward and back, maintaining a neutral spine

6. Differentiation between the front and back of the body

7. Neck and head control

POSITIVE SIGNS

☐ Able to tilt forward and backward without difficulty

☐ Able to maintain balance

☐ Relaxed body, shoulders, neck and facial muscles

☐ Able to maintain head control

☐ Able to maintain straight spine

NEGATIVE SIGNS

☐ The body flexes forward when tilting forward (e.g., neck, core muscles, arms, legs)

☐ The body extends backward when tilting back (e.g., neck, back, arms, legs)

☐ Fear of falling or falling

☐ Anxiousness and hesitation

☐ Stiffness or rigidity

☐ Body tension

3) HEAD PENDULUM WITH STRAIGHT ARMS

MATERIALS: None

OPTION 1: ARMS SHOULDER HEIGHT (IN FRONT)

1. Have the client stand with both feet flat on the floor and both arms straight, at shoulder height.

2. Observe if client can maintain step #1.

3. Ask client to extend their head to look up and hold for 5–7 seconds.

4. Go back to starting position (step #1).

5. Ask client to flex their head to look down on their feet for 5–7 seconds.

6. Repeat 1–3 times.

OPTION 2: ARMS OVERHEAD (STRAIGHT UP)

1. Have the client stand with both feet flat on the floor and both arms straight over their ears.

2. Observe if client can maintain step #1.

3. Ask client to extend their head to look up and hold for 5–7 seconds.

4. Go back to starting position (step #1).

5. Ask client to flex their head to look down on their feet for another 5–7 seconds.

6. Repeat 1–3 times.

GOALS

1. Balance and stability

2. Core strength and control

3. Differentiation between the upper body and lower body

4. Differentiation of the head from the rest of the body

5. Complete smooth and controlled movement, independently

POSITIVE SIGNS

- ☐ Able to move head up and down independently

- ☐ Shoulders and neck relaxed

- ☐ Able to keep balance

- ☐ Able to keep arms and legs straight

- ☐ Able to keep straight for an extended period of time

NEGATIVE SIGNS

- ☐ Unable to maintain balance and control

- ☐ Easily fatigued with arms extended

- ☐ Arms and legs might flex and extend with head movement

- ☐ Tension in neck and shoulders

- ☐ Back extension when head looks up

- ☐ Core flexion when head looks down

4) DOWN DOG & COBRA

MATERIALS: Yoga Mat

1. Have the client start on hands and knees, with palms on floor directly below the shoulders.

2. Ask client to lift knees off the floor, drop the head, and extend arms and legs while trying to maintain a straight spine (bend the knees if necessary).

3. Hold for 5–7 seconds.

4. Ask client to bend knees and slowly lower the body to the floor. Leave the lower body on the floor and initiate extension from the upper body to lift the head up. (Move as much as it feels comfortable.)

5. If it is safe and the client does not have back or neck injury, instruct them to push the floor with hands until both elbows are straight and eyes are gazing up.

6. Hold for 5–7 seconds.

GOALS

1. Flexion and extension of the entire body

2. Flexibility, strength and coordination

3. Upper body and lower body differentiation

4. Bilateral coordination

5. Core strength and flexibility

6. Shoulder stability and mobility

7. Motor planning and timing

8. Head control

POSITIVE SIGNS

☐ Able to sequence movements with ease

☐ Able to bring head up and down independently

☐ Able to keep tension off of neck and shoulders

☐ Able to flex the head to look down and extend it to look up with ease

☐ Able to motor plan and coordinate movements

☐ Able to transition from extension to flexion with ease

NEGATIVE SIGNS

- ☐ Stiff and jerky movements

- ☐ Pain and discomfort

- ☐ Unable to sequence movements correctly

- ☐ Difficulty initiating movement

- ☐ Tension in neck and shoulders

- ☐ Collapses to the floor and is unable to hold the body up for an extended period

MODIFICATIONS

- Work on flexibility

- Allow bent knees and extend one knee at a time

- Cat and Cow Exercise (refer to Book #3, STNR)

- If hamstrings and calves are too tight, keep knees bent

- Slightly march in place in Downdog pose to help with stretching calves and hamstrings

- Take multiple deep breaths while holding positions to release tension

5) ROLLING LIKE A LOG

Note: The TLR assists with the rolling milestone; it is necessary for brain development that a child learns to roll independently in both directions.

MATERIALS: Floor space for rolling; a visual straight line marked on the floor

1. Have the client lay down on the floor with the shoulders on top of the line and arms hanging beside the body.

2. Ask the client to roll while keeping the shoulders on the line.

3. If shoulders are not on the line, ask the client to adjust before rolling over again.

4. Roll back in the opposite direction.

5. Repeat 3–5 times.

GOALS

1. Bilateral coordination

2. Motor planning and timing

3. Body awareness

4. Right- and left-side discrimination

5. Crossing the midline

6. Gross motor skills

7. Spatial orientation

8. Visual perception, tracking, scanning and peripheral vision

POSITIVE SIGNS

☐ Able to roll on a straight line on either side

☐ Able to motor plan and move while keeping head level and off the floor

☐ Able to maintain core strength and stability

☐ Able to independently fix body position when not on the line

NEGATIVE SIGNS

☐ Difficulty aligning self on a straight line while rolling

☐ Difficulty lifting head off the floor to roll (e.g., head lag)

☐ Difficulty initiating movement

☐ Neck and shoulder tension and stress

6) SEGMENTAL ROLLING
(INITIATE FROM LOWER BODY)

MATERIALS: Floor space for rolling; a visual straight line marked on the floor

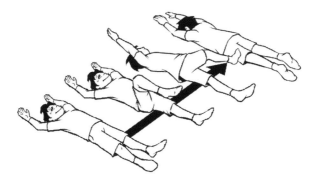

1. Have the client lay down on the floor with arms over the head and resting on the floor.

2. To initiate the roll, raise the right knee off the floor and bring it over the left; continue to twist the body until the right hip comes off the floor and the right upper body begins to roll over the left.

3. Allow the upper body to follow the lower body and roll over until the head is facing the floor.

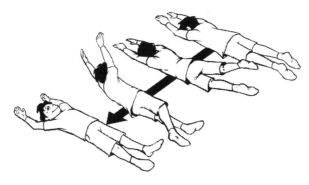

4. To roll back, lift the right leg and initiate the twist to the right side. Let the upper body follow the lower body until the body is back in the starting position.

5. Practice using the same mechanics to the right and to the left 3–5 times.

Note: Correct segmental rolling requires focus and body awareness. **As an instructor, you should practice this exercise and learn to feel it in your body before you begin to teach it to your clients.** Please encourage your client to take the time to notice the different muscles and body parts. Do this exercise slowly. It is best to do this exercise when you are working on stretching and body awareness. You can use this exercise with adults and older children to work on body awareness, right- and left-side discrimination, upper body and lower body discrimination, and focus.

GOALS

1. Bilateral coordination

2. Motor planning and timing

3. Stretching and flexibility

4. Body awareness

5. Right- and left-side discrimination

6. Upper body and lower body discrimination

7. Crossing the midline

8. Spatial orientation

9. Visual perception, tracking, scanning and peripheral vision

POSITIVE SIGNS

- ☐ Able to have fluid and controlled movements

- ☐ Able to differentiate the left and right sides of the body

- ☐ Able to differentiate the upper body from the lower body

- ☐ Able to roll and initiate rolling to either side

- ☐ Able to independently fix body position when not aligned

NEGATIVE SIGNS

- ☐ Unable to differentiate parts of the the body

- ☐ Awkward movement patterns

- ☐ Confusion and frustration

- ☐ Body parts move in unison

- ☐ May attempt to lift the head to flip over

- ☐ Neck and shoulder tension and stress

- ☐ Muscle weakness

- ☐ Poor flexibility

- ☐ Stiff and jerky movements

MODIFICATIONS

- Help client understand the difference between segmental rolling and moving in unison.

- Give tactile cues or physical support to motor plan movement and help the client know what part of the body to move.

7) SEGMENTAL ROLLING (INITIATE FROM UPPER BODY)

MATERIALS: Floor space for rolling; a visual straight line marked on the floor

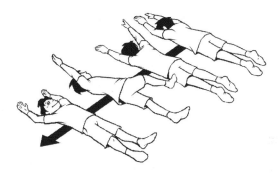

1. Have the client lay face down on the floor, with arms over the head and resting on the floor.

2. To initiate the roll, raise the right arm off the floor and bring it over to the right side of the head; continue to twist the body until the right shoulder comes off the floor and the right lower body begins to roll over.

3. Allow the lower body to follow the upper body and roll over until the head is facing up and resting on the floor.

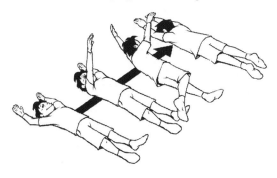

4. To roll back, lift the right arm and initiate the twist to the left side. Let the lower body follow the upper body until the body is back in the starting position.

5. Practice using the same mechanics to the right and to the left 3–5 times

Note: Make sure your client is cautious in these positions so as not to injure any part of their body. Give tactile cues to help your client initiate the correct movement.

GOALS

1. Bilateral coordination

2. Motor planning and timing

3. Visual perception, tracking, scanning and peripheral vision

4. Body awareness

5. Right- and left-side discrimination

6. Upper body and lower body discrimination

7. Crossing the midline

8. Spatial orientation

POSITIVE SIGNS

- ☐ Able to have fluid and controlled movements

- ☐ Able to differentiate the left and right sides of the body, and the upper body from the lower body

- ☐ Able to roll on a straight line on either side

- ☐ Able to independently fix body position when not on the line

NEGATIVE SIGNS

- ☐ Unable to differentiate parts of the the body

- ☐ Awkward movement patterns

- ☐ Confusion and frustration

- ☐ Body parts move in unison

- ☐ May attempt to lift the head to flip over

- ☐ Difficulty aligning self on a straight line while rolling

- ☐ Muscle weakness

- ☐ Poor flexibility

- ☐ Stiff and jerky movements

MODIFICATIONS

- • Help client understand the difference between segmental rolling and moving in unison.

- • Give tactile cues or physical support to motor plan movement and help the client know what part of the body to move.

8) THERABAND NECK RESISTANCE & TACTILE CUES

MATERIALS: Towel or Theraband

Note: This exercise is best done by older kids and adults.

---

1. Start by standing straight in a neutral spine position, with head straight.

2. Hold a Theraband with two hands, behind the head.

3. Maintain core stability and tension on Theraband.

4. Resist the band with head, without moving the hands.

5. Hold for 7–10 seconds.

6. Rest.

7. Repeat 5–7 times.

8. Switch the band to the front of the head, on the forehead.

9. Resist the band by pushing the band forward, without moving the arms.

10. Hold for 7-10 seconds.

11. Rest.

12. Repeat 5–7 times.

Note: This exercise can also influence other reflexes, such as the Symmetrical Tonic Neck Reflex (STNR) and the Moro Reflex.

GOALS

1. Head control and stability

2. Neck muscles exercise and strengthening

3. Isometric exercise

4. Balance and control

5. Body awareness

6. Muscle tone and posture

7. Upper body and shoulder strengthening

8. Core stability

POSITIVE SIGNS

☐ Able to maintain resistance on the band

☐ Able to maintaining a straight spine

☐ Able to keep the rest of the body stable

☐ Able to maintain balance and stability

NEGATIVE SIGNS

☐ Tension in neck and shoulders

☐ Unable to maintain resistance on the band

☐ Arms move in the direction of the head

☐ Over extension or flexion of the spine

☐ Might lose balance

MODIFICATION

If the client is unable to do the exercise independently, you can provide the resistance for them by using your hand.

1. Place your hand behind your client's head and invite them to resist you. (Please resist them slightly, just to activate their muscles.)

2. Hold for 5-7 seconds and rest.

3. Repeat 3-5 times.

4. Place your hand over your client's forehead and invite them to resist you. (Please resist them slightly, just to activate their muscles.)

5. Hold for 5-7 seconds and rest.

6. Repeat 3-5 times.

9) HEAD PENDULUM WITH BENT KNEES

MATERIALS: None

1. Have the client stand straight, with both feet flat on the floor.

2. Ask client to bend both knees while maintaining balance and alignment with the rest of the body; hold the position for 5–7 seconds.

Note: The head should stay straight and not be affected by knees bending.

3. Ask clients to extend their head to look up; hold for 5–7 seconds.

Note: Knees should stay bent and not be affected by the head extending.

4. Ask clients to flex their head to look down on their feet, holding for 5–7 seconds.

> **Note:** If the knees straighten when the head looks down, it might be an STNR retention. Please refer to Book #3.

GOALS

1. Balance and stability

2. Core strength and control

3. Head control

4. Muscle tone

5. Differentiation between the upper body and lower body

6. Differentiation of the head from the rest of the body

POSITIVE SIGNS

☐ Able to maintain straight spine when knees are bent

☐ Able to move head up and down independently

☐ Shoulders and neck relaxed

☐ Able to keep balance

NEGATIVE SIGNS

- ☐ Head moves forward when knees are bent

- ☐ Shoulder raises when knees are bent

- ☐ Loss of balance with head movement

- ☐ Extension of the knees, back or arms with head extension

- ☐ Tension and stress

- ☐ Fear of falling

10) JUMPING FORWARD

Note: The TLR assists with the jumping milestone; it is necessary for brain development that a child learns to jump independently in all directions.

MATERIALS: Chalk, tape or rope

1. Use chalk, tape or a rope to draw/make a line on the floor.

2. Start with both feet together; have client jump over the line and land on both feet.

GOALS

1. Bilateral coordination

2. Balance and stability

3. Motor planning and timing

4. Vestibular skill and proprioception

5. Body awareness

6. Spatial orientation and direction

7. Visual skills

8. Muscle tone and strength

POSITIVE SIGNS

☐ Able to jump with both feet

☐ Able to land on both feet

☐ Able to maintain balance

NEGATIVE SIGNS

☐ Afraid to jump

☐ Unable to coordinate movement

☐ Only lifts one leg off the ground

☐ Hesitation and confusion

11) HEAD PENDULUM STANDING ON TOES

MATERIALS: None

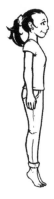

1. Have the client stand on their toes; check for balance.

2. Ask client to raise their head and look up for 3–5 seconds.

3. Observe that client is able to maintain balance.

4. Go back to starting position.

5. Ask client to look down on the floor for another 3–5 seconds.

6. Observe.

OBSERVATIONS

- Can they maintain balance while moving the head up and down?

- Can their head move independent of the rest of the body?

- Are they relaxed and maintaining steady breathing?

- Are there any parts of the body flexing and extending with the head?

- Were there shoulder movements and tension?

GOALS

1. Balance and stability

2. Core strength and control

3. Head control

4. Muscle tone

5. Differentiation between the upper body and lower body

6. Differentiation of the head from the rest of the body

POSITIVE SIGNS

☐ Able to move head up and down independently

☐ Shoulders and neck relaxed

☐ Able to keep balance

☐ Able to keep arms and legs straight

☐ Able to keep straight for an extended period of time

NEGATIVE SIGNS

- ☐ Unable to maintain balance and control

- ☐ Arms and legs might flex and extend with head movement

- ☐ Tension in neck and shoulders

- ☐ Back extension when head looks up

- ☐ Core flexion when head looks down

12) RAINBOW BREATHING

MATERIALS: None

1. Start by having the client stand with a neutral back.

2. Ask client to breathe out and squat down, with eyes looking down and palms together.

3. Hold for 1–3 seconds.

4. Ask clients to breathe in as they begin to stand, while extending their arms straight up over their head, open to the sides in the shape of the letter "V", and eyes looking up.

5. Breathe out while squatting back down.

6. Repeat 5–7 times.

GOALS

1. Balance and stability

2. Motor planning and coordination

3. Calming and deep breathing

4. Spatial awareness

5. Body awareness

6. Right- and left-side coordination

7. Upper body and lower body coordination and differentiation

8. Visual perception (scanning, tracking, focusing, peripheral vision, etc.)

POSITIVE SIGNS

☐ Able to maintain balance

☐ Able to coordinate arms and legs together

☐ Able to flex and extend the head without discomfort or unease

☐ Able to differentiate right and left sides of the body

☐ Able to maintain good posture

☐ Able to synchronize breathing with movement

NEGATIVE SIGNS

- ☐ Dizziness or nausea

- ☐ Loss of balance

- ☐ Inability to coordinate movement

- ☐ Disorientation and confusion

- ☐ Fear of falling and hesitation

13) BALANCE WALK

MATERIALS: Beanbag, balance beam

Note: Before starting this exercise, first check that your client can balance on a balance beam. If they can, continue with step #1.

1. Place a beanbag on client's head; balance it for 3–5 seconds.

2. Ask client to walk forward by alternating feet without dropping the bean bag.

GOALS

1. Upright posture and balance

2. Head alignment and control

3. Core stability and balance

4. Muscle tone

5. Bilateral coordination

6. Motor planning and timing

7. Spatial orientation and direction

8. Eye-foot coordination

9. Right- and left-side discrimination

10. Vestibular awareness

11. Proprioceptive awareness

12. Visual skill (peripheral vision, visual fixation, visual tracking)

POSITIVE SIGNS

☐ Able to maintain balance

☐ Able to coordinate movement

☐ Able to maintain upright posture

☐ Able to alternate feet with beanbag on head

☐ Able to maintain straight spine (posture)

NEGATIVE SIGNS

- ☐ Difficulty balancing

- ☐ Fear of falling

- ☐ Unable to alternate feet

- ☐ Falling off

- ☐ Unable to maintain straight spine

MODIFICATIONS

- If the balance beam is difficult, start with walking on a line. Focus on alternating feet and straight posture.

- Work on standing with straight posture.

- Hold on to clients' hands as they walk on a balance beam.

14) WALKING ON HEELS

MATERIALS: None

1. Ask your clients to lift their toes off the floor and stand on their heels.

2. Ask clients to walk forward, only on their heels, for about 10 - 15 feet.

GOALS

1. Bilateral coordination

2. Motor planning and timing

3. Spatial orientation

4. Body awareness

5. Right- and left-side discrimination

6. Posture and balance

7. Core stability and strength

8. Front and back body coordination

POSITIVE SIGNS

☐ Able to motor plan and coordinate smooth movement patterns

☐ Understands and executes movement independently

☐ Maintains balance and upright posture

☐ Able to walk on heels

NEGATIVE SIGNS

☐ Unable to coordinate and execute movement

☐ Difficulty staying upright

☐ Loses balance

☐ Leg cramps and complaints

15) SUPERMAN & SUPERWOMAN

MATERIALS: None

1. Start with the body flat on the floor, arms extended, and the head in a neutral position.

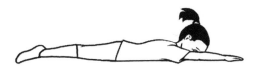

2. Lift the arms and legs off the floor and gaze forward.

3. Hold for 5–10 seconds.

4. Rest.

5. Repeat 3–5 times.

GOALS

1. Core stability and strength

2. Bilateral coordination

3. Back extension and strength

4. Motor planning and timing

5. Body awareness

6. Posture and alignment

7. Muscle tone

8. Flexibility

9. Head control and stability

10. Upper body and lower body coordination and differentiation

POSITIVE SIGNS

☐ Able to lift both arms and legs off the floor simultaneously

☐ Able to lift head off the ground and gaze forward

☐ Maintains balance, and lifts with straight legs and arms

☐ Shoulders relaxed

☐ Steady breathing and calmness

NEGATIVE SIGNS

- ☐ Unable to lift head off the floor

- ☐ Unable to lift arms and legs off the floor

- ☐ Tension in neck and shoulders

- ☐ Complains of pain and discomfort

- ☐ Uneven lift of arms and legs; may rock from side to side to keep balance

- ☐ Bent or twisted legs

- ☐ Bent elbows or shrugged shoulders

MODIFICATIONS

- Start by lifting only the upper body and leave the lower body on the floor.

- Lift only the lower body; leave the head and upper body on the floor.

- If clients are unable to lift their arms or legs, you can provide physical cues or resistance opposite to the direction you want them to go. For example, slightly resist their arms down and ask them to push up against you. The tactile and proprioceptive cues can "wake up" their muscles and help their brain know which muscles need to fire up. The brain and body can work together; however, due to retained reflexes, confusion or lack of use, information might not be reaching the right parts. We can provide tactile cues to help facilitate those situations.

FUN WITH SCOOTER BOARD

For younger kids who are not yet able to follow a step-by-step exercise, you can use scooter board activities to target specific muscle groups and retained reflexes. There are several fun games, obstacle courses and activities you can do using the activities listed below. Remember if your client has several retained reflexes, the variety of head movements and body positioning can trigger those reflex patterns and affect coordination. The reflexes to keep in mind when doing the exercises listed below are: the Moro, ATNR, Landau, Palmar (Grasp) and STNR. For additional scooter board exercises, please refer to Book #3, An Interactive Guide to the Symmetrical Tonic Neck Reflex (STNR).

16) SUPERWOMAN/SUPERMAN ON SCOOTER

MATERIALS: Scooter Board

1. Start by laying prone (on belly) on a scooter board and propel self, using both hands on the floor.

2. Lift both arms and legs off the floor but keep them straight, and "fly" forward with arms and hands outstretched.

3. Repeat as many times as needed.

GOALS

1. Core stability and strength

2. Bilateral coordination

3. Back extension and strength

4. Motor planning and timing

5. Body awareness

6. Posture and alignment

7. Muscle tone and flexibility

8. Vestibular input

9. Head control and stability

10. Upper body and lower body coordination and differentiation

POSITIVE SIGNS

☐ Able to lift both arms and legs off the floor simultaneously

☐ Able to lift head up and gaze forward

☐ Maintains balance, and lifts with straight legs and arms

☐ Shoulders relaxed

☐ Steady breathing and calmness

NEGATIVE SIGNS

☐ Unable to lift head up to gaze forward

☐ Unable to lift arms and legs off the floor

☐ Tension in neck and shoulders

☐ Complains of pain and discomfort

☐ Uneven lift with arms and legs

☐ May rock from side to side to keep balance

☐ Bent or twisted legs

☐ Bent elbows or shrugged shoulders

17) SCOOTER BOARD ROPE PULL (TWO HANDS)

MATERIALS: Scooter Board, rope and/or obstacle course

Note: If the client cannot hold on to a rope, check for Palmar (Grasp) Reflex retention. To make the activities more challenging, use a shorter scooter board.

1. Start by laying prone (on belly) on a scooter board and holding a rope with two hands.

2. Ask your client to lift like a superman/superwoman, and maintain back extension with straight arms and legs, while holding onto the rope.

3. Pull your client while they are maintaining the position.

4. Repeat as many times as needed.

GOALS

1. Core stability and strength

2. Bilateral coordination

3. Back extension and strength

4. Motor planning and timing

5. Body awareness

6. Posture and alignment

7. Muscle tone and flexibility

8. Vestibular input

9. Head control and stability

10. Upper body and lower body coordination and differentiation

POSITIVE SIGNS

☐ Able to lift both arms and legs off the floor simultaneously

☐ Able to lift head up and gaze forward

☐ Able to hold onto the rope while being pulled

☐ Maintains balance, and lifts with straight legs and arms

☐ Shoulders relaxed

☐ Steady breathing and calmness

NEGATIVE SIGNS

- ☐ Unable to hold onto the rope while being pulled

- ☐ Unable to lift head up to gaze forward

- ☐ Unable to lift arms and legs off the floor

- ☐ Unable to extend or straighten the arms

- ☐ Tension in neck and shoulders

- ☐ Complains of pain and discomfort

- ☐ Fatigue and discomfort

18) SCOOTER BOARD ROPE PULL (ALTERNATING HANDS)

MATERIALS: Scooter Board and rope

Note: If the client cannot hold on to a rope, check for Palmar (Grasp) Reflex retention. To make the activities more challenging, use a shorter scooter board.

---

1. Start by laying prone (on belly) on a scooter board and holding onto a rope with two hands.

2. Ask your client to lift like a superman/superwoman, and maintain back extension with straight arms and legs, while holding onto the rope.

3. Ask your client to pull on the rope using alternating hands to propel self forward.

4. Repeat as many times as needed.

GOALS

1. Core stability and strength

2. Bilateral coordination

3. Back extension and strength

4. Motor planning and timing

5. Body awareness

6. Posture and alignment

7. Vestibular input

8. Muscle tone and flexibility

9. Head control and stability

10. Upper body and lower body coordination and differentiation

POSITIVE SIGNS

☐ Able to lift both arms and legs off the floor simultaneously

☐ Able to lift head up and gaze forward

☐ Able to hold onto the rope and use alternate hands to pull self forward

☐ Maintains balance, and lifts with straight legs and arms

☐ Shoulders relaxed

☐ Steady breathing and calmness

NEGATIVE SIGNS

☐ Unable to hold onto the rope while pulling self forward

☐ Unable to lift head up to gaze forward

☐ Unable to lift arms and legs off the floor

☐ Tension in neck and shoulders

☐ Complains of pain and discomfort

19) WALL PUSH ON SCOOTER BOARD

MATERIALS: Scooter Board

Note: Please make sure that you have enough space for the client to do this exercise. You can also stand behind clients to make sure they do not crash into something dangerous.

---

1. Start by laying prone (on belly) on a scooter board facing a wall.

2. Ask the client to get as close as they can to the wall and push themselves backward.

3. Remind client to keep both legs straight.

4. Repeat as many times as needed.

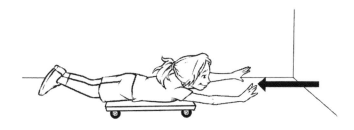

GOALS

1. Core stability and strength

2. Bilateral coordination

3. Back extension and strength

4. Motor planning and timing

5. Body awareness

6. Posture and alignment

7. Vestibular input

8. Muscle tone and flexibility

9. Head control and stability

10. Upper body and lower body coordination and differentiation

POSITIVE SIGNS

☐ Able to lift both arms and legs off the floor simultaneously

☐ Able to lift head up and gaze forward

☐ Able to push off the wall while maintaining back and leg extension

☐ Maintains balance, and lifts with straight legs and arms

NEGATIVE SIGNS

☐ Unable to push off the wall while maintaining back extension and straight legs

☐ Unable to lift head up to gaze forward

☐ Unable to lift arms and legs off the floor

☐ Legs might flex with arms (e.g., when arms bend to push away from wall, the legs might bend with them)

☐ Tension in neck and shoulders

20) SCOOTER BOARD SLITHER ON BACK

MATERIALS: Scooter Board

> **Note:** Please make sure your client has enough space to move around to do the following activity.

1. Client starts by laying on back on a scooter board, with head hovering and both feet on the floor.

2. Maintain balance and control.

3. Ask your client to move back by propelling self with hands and feet for 10-15 feet.

4. Rest.

5. Repeat as many times as needed.

VARIATION

☐ Spin around in circles while on back on scooter board.

GOALS

1. Upper body strengthening

2. Shoulder stability

3. Upper body and lower body differentiation

4. Motor planning and timing

5. Bilateral coordination

6. Balance and stability

7. Directionality

8. Visual skills

9. Core and neck strength and stability

10. Right- and left-side discrimination

11. Vestibular input

POSITIVE SIGNS

- ☐ Able to hold body up in a curled position

- ☐ Able to maintain head control

- ☐ Able to move while maintaining core stability

NEGATIVE SIGNS

- ☐ Unable to hold head up

- ☐ Unable to motor plan movements

- ☐ Fear of falling and anxiety

Reminder: We know that several reflexes can be triggered simultaneously when using a play-based approach. We advise that you use your clinical reasoning skills and understanding of other reflexes to structure the treatment session.

21) SCOOTER BOARD ON BACK (LEGS ONLY)

MATERIALS: Scooter Board

1. Ask clients to lay on their back on scooter board, cross hands over their chest and use only their legs to propel themselves.

2. Create an obstacle the child can use to help with interaction and interest.

3. Repeat as many times as needed.

GOALS

1. Bilateral coordination

2. Upper body strengthening

3. Shoulder stability

4. Head control

5. Upper body and lower body differentiation

6. Motor planning and timing

7. Balance and control

8. Vestibular input

9. Core and neck strength and stability

10. Right- and left-side discrimination

POSITIVE SIGNS

☐ Able to hold body up in a curled position

☐ Able to hold and balance the head up

☐ Able to use only the legs to propel self

☐ Able to motor plan movement while maintaining core stability

NEGATIVE SIGNS

☐ Unable to hold head up

☐ Unable to balance and hold the head up

☐ Unable to motor plan movement while maintaining core stability

☐ Fear of falling and anxiety

22) WALL KICK ON SCOOTER BOARD

MATERIALS: Scooter Board

Note: Please make sure that you have enough space for the client to do this exercise. You can also stand behind clients to make sure they do not crash into something dangerous.

---

1. Have the client lay supine on floor, with head curled forward and hands together.

2. Place both feet on the wall and push against the wall.

3. While sliding back, ask the client to maintain the curled position for about 1-3 seconds.

4. Repeat 3-5 times.

GOALS

1. Motor planning and timing

2. Upper body and lower body differentiation

3. Core strength and stability

4. Neck and shoulder stability and control

5. Head control

6. Bilateral coordination

7. Muscle tone and flexibility

POSITIVE SIGNS

☐ Able to balance self on scooter board

☐ Fluid movement and coordination

☐ Flexed neck and balanced

☐ Able to flex and extend legs to push against the wall

☐ Maintains balance and stability

NEGATIVE SIGNS

☐ Unable to coordinate movement

☐ Body arches backward, making movement difficult to push against a wall

- ☐ Movement overflow (e.g., facial grimaces; arms and hands opening and closing)

- ☐ Unable to lift feet off the floor

- ☐ Difficulty balancing (e.g., may fall over or rock back and forth)

- ☐ Head might go back (extends) when kicking against the wall

- ☐ Fear of falling and anxiety

23) POPCORN ON FLOOR

MATERIALS: Yoga Mat

1. Have the client lie down, supine on a yoga mat, with arms and legs extended.

2. Encourage the client to bring chin to the chest, and curl up by hugging knees with hands.

3. Hold for 3–5 seconds.

4. In a smooth and controlled movement, have the client bring the body back to its original position.

5. Repeat 5–10 times.

GOALS

1. Core strength and balance

2. Muscle tone, motor planning and timing

3. Right- and left-side discrimination and differentiation

4. Upper body and lower body coordination and differentiation

5. Head control and alignment

POSITIVE SIGNS

☐ Able to lift the head off the floor

☐ Able to maintain head flexion alignment and balance

☐ Able to balance the body in full body flexion without rocking side to side

☐ Smooth arm and leg movements

☐ Steady breathing

NEGATIVE SIGNS:

☐ Head lagging behind when trying to curl up

☐ Body rocking left to right or falling over

☐ Unable to bring the body into a curled (flexed) position

☐ Facial grimacing or tongue sticking out

☐ Tension in neck and shoulders

VARIATION

☐ Popcorn on Therapy Ball (Refer to Book #1, Moro Reflex)

24) SWIMMING ON FLOOR

MATERIALS: None

1. Start with the body flat on the floor, arms extended, and head in a neutral position.

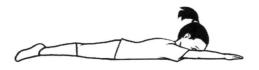

2. Lift the arms and legs off the floor and gaze forward.

SWIMMING ON FLOOR (SAME SIDES)

3. Raise the left arm and leg while simultaneously lowering the right arm and leg.

4. Then raise the right arm and leg while simultaneously lowering the left arm and leg.

5. Repeat 7–10 times.

6. Raise the right arm and left leg higher while keeping the opposite sides lower.

7. Raise the left arm and right leg higher while keeping the opposite sides lower.

8. Repeat 7–10 times.

GOALS

1. Core stability and strength

2. Bilateral coordination

3. Back extension and strength

4. Motor planning and timing

5. Body awareness

6. Posture and alignment

7. Muscle tone

8. Flexibility

9. Head control and stability

10. Upper body and lower body coordination and differentiation

POSITIVE SIGNS

- ☐ Able to lift both arms and legs up at the same time

- ☐ Able to lift head off the ground and gaze forward, and maintain balance and lift

- ☐ Relaxed shoulders and neck

- ☐ Straight arms and legs

- ☐ Steady breathing and calmness

- ☐ Able to differentiate between the right and the left sides of the body

- ☐ Able to alternate arms and legs at the same time

NEGATIVE SIGNS

- ☐ Unable to lift head off the ground

- ☐ Unable to lift head, arms and legs off the ground

- ☐ Unable to differentiate between the right and the left sides of the body

- ☐ Unable to alternate arms and legs at the same time

- ☐ Tension in neck and shoulders (e.g., raised and squeezed shoulders)

- ☐ Uneven lift with arms and legs (e.g., may rock side to side to keep balance)

- ☐ Bent or twisted legs

- ☐ Bent elbows

- ☐ Confusion of the right and left sides of the body

25) EARTH HUGGER (BACKWARDS)

MATERIALS: Yoga Mat

1. Have the client lay face down on the mat, with arms extended.

2. Ask the client to press down, as if giving a full-body hug to the floor.

3. Check to see if the client is pressing down by gently attempting to lift the client's arms and legs upward.

4. Ask the client to hold the position for 5–7 seconds while you are checking.

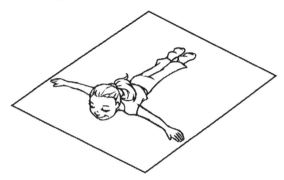

5. Now, ask the client to **lift only the head** while pressing down on the floor with arms and legs.

6. Hold for 5–7 seconds.

7. Repeat 3–5 times.

Note: The head must face down. The turning of the head to the right or the left will activate the Asymmetrical Tonic Neck Reflex (ATNR). If necessary, provide physical head support to maintain face down position.

GOALS

1. Maintain equal resistance in all four extremities

2. Bilateral coordination

3. Right- and left-side discrimination and differentiation

4. Upper body and lower body coordination and differentiation

5. Core strength and muscle tone

6. Head control and alignment

7. Neck control and stability

8. Muscle tone and posture

POSITIVE SIGNS

- ☐ Able to motor plan sequence
- ☐ Extremities pressing down on the floor
- ☐ Similar pressure in all extremities
- ☐ Able to lift head off (extension) the floor
- ☐ Even and steady breathing
- ☐ Able to extend the neck with ease

NEGATIVE SIGNS

- ☐ Unable to press down equally with both arms and legs
- ☐ Unequal pressure within the extremities
- ☐ Unable to lift head off the floor
- ☐ Neck and shoulder tension
- ☐ Facial grimaces or tongue sticking out
- ☐ Overarching or hips hiking up
- ☐ Difficulty isolating the neck from the rest of the body
- ☐ Holding breath and stressed
- ☐ The rest of the body might want to extend or lift off the floor
- ☐ Might see extension on the rest of the body

26) EARTH HUGGER (FORWARD)

MATERIALS: Yoga Mat

1. Have the client lay face up on the mat, with arms extended.

2. Ask the client to press down, as if pushing the floor downward.

3. Check to see if the client is pressing down by gently trying to lift the client's arms and legs upward.

4. Have the client hold that position for 5–7 seconds while you check arms and legs.

5. Ask the client to lift only the head while pressing down on the floor with arms and legs.

6. Hold for 5–7 seconds.

7. Repeat 3–5 times.

Note: The client's head must face up. The turning of the head to the right or the left will activate the Asymmetrical Tonic Neck Reflex (ATNR). If necessary, provide physical head support to maintain face up position.

GOALS

1. Maintain equal resistance in all four extremities

2. Bilateral coordination

3. Right- and left-side discrimination and differentiation

4. Upper body and lower body coordination and differentiation

5. Core strength and muscle tone

6. Head control and alignment

7. Neck control and stability

8. Muscle tone and posture

POSITIVE SIGNS

☐ Able to motor plan sequence

☐ Extremities pressing down on the floor

☐ Similar pressure in all extremities

☐ Able to lift head off (flexion) the floor

☐ Even and steady breathing

☐ Able to flex the neck with ease

NEGATIVE SIGNS

- ☐ Unable to press down equally with both arms and legs

- ☐ Unequal pressure within the extremities

- ☐ Unable to lift head off the floor

- ☐ Neck and shoulder tension

- ☐ Facial grimaces or tongue sticking out

- ☐ Overarching or hips hiking up

- ☐ Difficulty isolating the neck from the rest of the body

- ☐ Holding breath and stressed

- ☐ The rest of the body might want to flex (e.g., arms and legs)

- ☐ Might see flexion on the rest of the body

27) HOT POTATOES

MATERIALS: Yoga Mat and a 12" ball

1. Have the client lie down on their back on a mat.

2. Have the client hold a light basketball-sized ball with both hands over the head.

3. Ask the client to transfer the ball from hands to feet.

4. Both feet and arms should reach towards the mat without arching the back.

5. Maintaining the hold, pass the ball from feet back to hands.

6. Repeat 5–10 times.

GOALS

1. Able to bring legs and arms together

2. Isolation and differentiation of upper body and lower body

3. Bilateral coordination

4. Core strength and trunk control

5. Muscle tone and strength

6. Visual perception

POSITIVE SIGNS

☐ Able to coordinate both sides of the body

☐ Able to sustain smooth and controlled movement

☐ Maintains sufficient upper body, trunk and lower body strength

☐ Able to keep head on the floor

NEGATIVE SIGNS

- ☐ Unable to maintain smooth and controlled movement

- ☐ Unable to transfer the ball between hands and legs

- ☐ Shoulder tension and facial grimaces

- ☐ Unable to lift both legs off the floor

- ☐ Overarching of the back

FOR TEENAGERS AND ADULTS

A Pilates Instructor will be ideal for working on the following exercises.

The following activities are best used with older children, teenagers and adults. The exercises are all inspired by the Pilates Method and can be adapted into a treatment session. For more support and guidance, feel free to refer to our online consultation program.

Pilates is one of the most effective methods that I have used myself to help recover from injuries, and learn to isolate and activate challenging muscles. I noticed that by helping isolate certain muscles and focusing on integrating specific reflexes, we can improve our posture, strength and flexibility. In this section, I have put together some of the exercises that I think are easier to implement in your clinical setting or for personal development with minimal training. Please note that these activities can be as easy or difficult as you are willing to make them.

If you or your client has back or neck injuries, please be very careful and use your clinical judgment and/or consult with a physician.

28) BOAT POSE

MATERIALS: Mat

1. Start in a seated position with knees bent, feet flat, and arms extended forward.

Note: Do not round your back!

2. Lift feet off the floor and balance for 2–3 seconds.

ADVANCED

3. Extend legs to create a "V" shape with torso and legs.

4. Breathe comfortably and pause every 3 seconds.

5. Repeat 3-5 times.

GOALS

1. Muscle tone and flexibility

2. Head control and alignment

3. Core strength and stability

4. Shoulder strength and stability

5. Posture and balance

6. Body awareness

7. Right- and left-side discrimination

8. Bilateral coordination

9. Motor planning and timing

10. Spatial orientation

11. Visual skill (peripheral vision, visual fixation, visual tracking)

POSITIVE SIGNS

☐ Able to motor plan and coordinate smooth movement patterns

☐ Understands and executes movement independently

☐ Differentiates right and left sides of the body

☐ Differentiates upper body from lower body

☐ Maintains balance and postural control

☐ Able to maintain head control

NEGATIVE SIGNS

- ☐ Unable to coordinate and execute movement

- ☐ Rocks back and forth, and unable to maintain balance

- ☐ Unable to lift head off the floor

- ☐ Difficulty maintaining head control

- ☐ Head might extend when legs extend

- ☐ Lack of core strength

- ☐ Head might be tucked in

- ☐ Tension in shoulders and neck

29) BOAT POSE CRUNCHES

MATERIALS: Mat

1. Start in a seated position with knees bent, feet flat, and arms extended forward.

Note: Do not round your back!

2. Extend the legs and hold for 1-3 seconds.

3. Lower both upper and lower body, hovering but not touching the floor, then rise back up.

4. Repeat 3-5 times.

GOALS

1. Core stability and strength

2. Posture and balance

3. Bilateral coordination

4. Motor planning and timing

5. Crossing the midline

6. Spatial orientation

7. Visual skill (e.g., peripheral, fixation, tracking)

8. Body awareness

9. Right- and left-side differentiation

10. Upper body and lower body differentiation

POSITIVE SIGNS

☐ Able to motor plan and coordinate smooth movement patterns

☐ Understands and executes movement independently

☐ Differentiates right and left sides of the body

☐ Differentiates upper body from lower body

☐ Maintains balance and postural control

☐ Maintains head control and stability

NEGATIVE SIGNS

- [ ] Unable to coordinate and execute movement

- [ ] Rocks back and forth, and unable to maintain balance

- [ ] Unable to maintain head control

- [ ] Tension in neck and shoulders

- [ ] Holds breath

- [ ] Arches back

- [ ] Upper body slouching

MODIFICATIONS

- Work on each step until it is mastered and only move onto the next when client is ready

- Do the exercise with bent knees

- Start by lowering either the lower or upper body

- Focus more on core and back strengthening, and activation exercises

30) BICYCLE CURLS (CRISS-CROSS CURLS)

MATERIALS: None

1. Start with a flat back on the floor, with knees bent and hands on the back of the head.

2. Bring hands on the back of the head up and curl up. Bring both knees up.

3. Twist the upper body to the left and tap the left knee with the right elbow.

4. Then, twist the upper body to the right and tap the right knee with the left elbow.

5. Maintain flexion of the body while you repeat 7–10 times.

GOALS

1. Head control

2. Core stability and strength

3. Posture and balance

4. Bilateral coordination

5. Motor planning and timing

6. Crossing the midline

7. Spatial orientation

8. Visual skill (e.g., peripheral, fixation, tracking)

9. Body awareness

10. Right- and left-side discrimination

POSITIVE SIGNS

☐ Able to motor plan and coordinate smooth movement patterns

☐ Understands and executes movement independently

☐ Differentiates right and left sides of the body

☐ Maintains balance and upright posture

NEGATIVE SIGNS

☐ Unable to coordinate and execute movement

☐ Difficulty twisting to the opposite side

☐ Tension in neck and shoulders

☐ Unable to maintain head control

31) ROLLING LIKE A BALL

MATERIALS: Mat

1. Start by pulling knees towards your body and create a "C" shape with the spine. Eyes should be gazing down.

2. Begin by lifting the feet off the floor and balancing for a few seconds. Maintain tension between the front and back muscles.

3. Roll back all the way to the upper back and shoulders, then roll forward.

4. Repeat 5–7 times.

GOALS

1. Core stability and strength

2. Posture and balance

3. Bilateral coordination

4. Motor planning and timing

5. Head and shoulder control

6. Spatial orientation

7. Visual skill (e.g., peripheral, fixation, tracking)

8. Body awareness

9. Right- and left-side discrimination

10. Upper body and lower body discrimination and coordination

POSITIVE SIGNS

☐ Able to motor plan and coordinate smooth movement patterns

☐ Able to keep a "C" spinal curve while rocking back and forth

☐ Organizes and differentiates upper and lower body

☐ Maintains balance and head control

NEGATIVE SIGNS

☐ Unable to coordinate and execute movement

☐ Rocks side to side and unable to maintain balance

☐ Difficulty maintaining head control

☐ Unable to keep a "C" spinal curve while rocking back and forth

☐ Back or neck extension when rolling back

☐ When rocking back, the head and back might extend

☐ When rocking back, the head might lag behind

☐ Neck and shoulder tension

32) DEAD BUG

MATERIALS: Mat

1. Start on the floor with a flat back and head resting comfortably, with knees and shoulders at a 90 degree angle.

2. Lower the right leg and the left arm to hover over the floor.

3. Bring arm and leg back to starting position.

4. Lower the left leg and the right arm, hovering them over the floor.

5. Bring arm and leg back to starting position.

6. Repeat 7–10 times.

7. Curl neck and lift head off the floor. Bring knees parallel to hips while keeping arms straight.

8. Bring the right arm and the right leg forward, and the left arm and left leg backward.

9. Bring the left arm and the left leg forward, and the right arm and right leg backward.

10. This is one full set.

11. Repeat 3–5 times.

GOALS

1. Core stability and strength

2. Bilateral coordination

3. Motor planning and timing

4. Head and neck control

5. Spatial orientation and direction

6. Visual skill (peripheral vision, visual fixation, visual tracking)

7. Body awareness

8. Right- and left-side discrimination

9. Posture and balance

10. Upper body and lower body differentiation and coordination

11. Shoulder strength and control

12. Coordination of both sides of the body

POSITIVE SIGNS

☐ Able to coordinate both sides of the body

☐ Able to isolate extremities and hold the head neutral

☐ Able to maintain steady breathing

☐ Able to maintain relaxed shoulders and neck

NEGATIVE SIGNS

- ☐ Unable to isolate extremities

- ☐ Head lagging and difficult to lift off the floor

- ☐ Opposite side of the body mimics the movement of the one that is moving

- ☐ (e.g., extreme movement or slight twitching of flexion and extension)

- ☐ Unable to balance head or body in flexed position

- ☐ Tension in shoulders and neck

- ☐ Unsteady breathing

33) DOUBLE LEG STRETCH

MATERIALS: Mat

1. Start flat on the mat, with a neutral spine, and neck and head relaxed.

2. Curl neck and lift head off the mat; bring knees to chest and hold the shins with hands. Hold for 1–3 seconds.

Note: Work on balance and control here. If there is no back and/or neck pain, move to the next step.

3. (Breath → Inhale) Simultaneously extend the legs and arms, while maintaining head and core stability.

4. (Breath → Exhale) Bring the arms and knees together, and squeeze the shins to create tension.

5. Repeat 3–5 times.

GOALS

1. Core strength and stability

2. Posture and balance

3. Body awareness

4. Head and neck control

5. Upper body and lower body differentiation and coordination

6. Shoulder strength, stability and control

7. Muscle tone and flexibility

8. Bilateral coordination

9. Motor planning and timing

10. Spatial orientation and direction

11. Visual skill (peripheral vision, visual fixation, visual tracking)

12. Right- and left-side discrimination and coordination

POSITIVE SIGNS

☐ Able to coordinate both sides of the body equally

☐ Able to isolate extremities and hold the head neutral

☐ Able to maintain steady breathing

☐ Able to flex the head and maintain balance

☐ Able to maintain relaxed shoulders and neck

NEGATIVE SIGNS

- ☐ Unable to isolate extremities

- ☐ Head lagging and difficult to lift off the floor

- ☐ Head moves with extremities (e.g., when extremities extend, the head might extend and when the extremities flex, the head might flex)

- ☐ Unable to balance the head or body

- ☐ Tension in shoulders and neck

- ☐ Unsteady breathing

MODIFICATIONS

- • Work on balance and control, step #2.

- • Support the head with hands and only move the legs.

34) BANANA ROLL

MATERIALS: Mat

> **Note:** This is an advanced exercise. Make sure your client can place the lower back flat on the floor and maintain body control before doing this exercise.

1. Start with the lower back flat on the floor, with knees up and arms straight. (Refer to Dead Bug, Exercise #32 above, step #7.)

2. Extend both arms and legs out to create an imaginary "banana" by engaging the core muscles.

3. Hold for 2–3 seconds.

4. Roll to the left, while maintaining arm and leg extensions without touching the floor, by engaging the back extension muscles.

5. Hold the extension for 2–3 seconds.

6. Roll back to the starting position, while keeping all muscles engaged. Hold for 2–3 seconds.

7. Practice rolling in both directions.

8. Rest.

9. Repeat for 3–5 sets.

GOALS

1. Motor planning and timing

2. Right- and left-side discrimination and differentiation

3. Upper body and lower body coordination and differentiation

4. Core strength and muscle tone

5. Head control and alignment

6. Whole body alignment

7. Whole body flexion and extension

POSITIVE SIGNS

☐ Able to lift the head off the floor and maintain balance

☐ Able to balance the body in full body flexion and extension

☐ Able to roll and maintain balance and head control

☐ Steady breathing

NEGATIVE SIGNS

- [ ] Head lagging behind

- [ ] Body rocking left to right when trying to balance

- [ ] Unable to bring the body in full flexion and extension position

- [ ] Tension in neck and shoulders

MODIFICATIONS

- Superman/Superwoman (Exercise #15)

- Popcorn on Floor (Exercise #23)

- Dead Bug (Exercise #32)

35) BACK EXTENSION ON THERAPY BALL

MATERIALS: Therapy Ball

1. Bring hands to the back of the head and support the head.

Note: First, work on balancing on a therapy ball without falling over. After this step is achieved, move to the next steps.

---

2. (Breath → Inhale) Extend the back and balance for 1–3 seconds.

3. (Breath → Exhale) Curl the upper body over the ball.

4. Repeat 5–7 times and rest.

GOALS

1. Upper body strengthening

2. Shoulder stability

3. Upper body and lower body differentiation

4. Motor planning and timing

5. Bilateral coordination

6. Balance and stability

7. Core and neck strength and stability

8. Right- and-left side discrimination

POSITIVE SIGNS

☐ Able to balance on a therapy ball using core muscles and legs

☐ Able to keep the lower body stable when the upper body and head are moving up and down

☐ Able to keep tension off of neck and shoulders

☐ Steady breathing

NEGATIVE SIGNS

☐ Unable to isolate the upper body from the lower body

☐ Unable to fully straighten upper body

- ☐ Difficulty keeping the lower body straight when the upper body is in a flexed position (e.g., knees might bend)

- ☐ Unable to maintain balance on the therapy ball while moving (e.g., vestibular and strength challenges)

- ☐ Unable to keep head balanced

- ☐ Tension in neck and shoulders

MODIFICATIONS

- If there is tightness and tension in the back of the legs (e.g., hamstrings and calves), start by marching in place to warm up the muscles and improve flexibility.

- Help balance the ball for your clients until they are able to balance on their own.

CHAPTER 5

ADDITIONAL RECOMMENDATIONS AND RESOURCES

A. HOW DO YOU KNOW IF A TREATMENT PLAN AND EXERCISES ARE WORKING?

Parents often view their children subjectively and have a hard time seeing the gradual changes their children are making with treatment. I created a checklist to help parents more objectively see their child's development. The same list can also be used to determine if the treatment plan is not working. At times, a child may regress, and this should prompt the care provider to change the approach to treatment.

To make this routine easier for non-professionals to implement, I have created an additional list for monitoring progress and a letter of encouragement to parents who are working on the TLR with their child. The following list is one that I created with my own children and students. Make sure to add other symptoms and areas that you might observe that I have not included. This list can also include goals you are working on or goals parents have that relate to the TLR. What is on the list depends on the individual client, and the goal is to observe and note visible improvements. After about 6–8 weeks of constant reflex integration exercises, you should begin seeing changes. If, for any reason, there is no improvement, go back and examine your treatment plan.

B. SUGGESTED MOVEMENT BREAKS AND ACTIVITIES TO HELP PROMOTE TONIC LABYRINTHINE REFLEX (TLR) INTEGRATION

To help increase the number of opportunities the child gets to practice, incorporate movement breaks that target the TLR throughout the day. One way to do this is by creating the child's movement breaks to address the TLR. While creating the child's movement activities, be careful not to frustrate the child by demanding an exercise that is too difficult for them. You want the child to ease into movements and preferably initiate the games themselves. Give the child options. These movement breaks should focus on integrating the TLR gently and gradually. Please use your clinical judgment and knowledge of the child while you are creating this plan. Below are the suggested activities to get you started.

TABLE #2: SUGGESTED ACTIVITIES TO INCORPORATE THROUGHOUT THE DAY

VESTIBULAR	POSTURE
• Any of the Scooter Board exercises • Rolling exercises • Rolling Like a Ball • Banana Roll • Rainbow Breathing • Head Pendulum Exercises • Jumping exercises	• Head Pendulum Exercises • Theraband Neck Resistant • Balance Walk • Whole Body Pendulum • Earth Hugger Forward • Earth Hugger Backward
VISUAL	**BACK EXTENSION**
• Any of the Scooter Board exercises • Rolling exercises • Rainbow Breathing • Balance Walk • Walking on Heels • Head Pendulum Exercises • Jumping exercises	• Down Dog & Cobra • Superwoman & Superman • Scooter Board Rope Pull • Wall Push on Scooter Board • Swimming on Floor • Back Extension on Therapy Ball • Banana Roll

Table #2: Suggested Activities to Incorporate Throughout the Day

Visit https://ritp.info/tlr-book for downloadable version.

C. TREATMENT IDEAS FOR OCCUPATIONAL THERAPISTS WORKING IN A CLINICAL SETTING

There are a variety of games and activities you can incorporate to address the TLR. The challenge may be grading the activity to meet children at their level while maintaining excitement and fun.

- Most exercises, games and tools in the clinic can directly or indirectly trigger the TLR. Use your clinical judgment to set up your treatment session.

- Collaborate with a vision therapist to address the visual skills, and get proper screening to rule out a vision skill problem.

- While positioning your client in the variety of the activities above to trigger the TLR, additional reflexes, such as the Moro, STNR and Landau, might also be triggered. Please refer to the appropriate books for more information.

- Incorporate therapy equipment, such as:

  o Swings (e.g., Bolster, Moon, Trapeze, Platform and Frog)

  o Hanging down from bolster swing

  o Hanging and swinging from a trapeze

  o Riding on a scooter board

  o Rocking back and forth on a therapy ball, etc.

- If you are trained in the following tools, incorporate them in your sessions. Here are some suggestions:

  o Masgutova Method (MNRI)

  o Rhythmic Movement Training (RMTi)

o   Listening programs, such as Integrated Listening Systems (iLs)

o   Interactive Metronome (IM)

o   Brain Gym and other movement exercises you think are beneficial in your clinical settings.

D. LETTER TO PARENT/CAREGIVER

Dear Parents,

When the Tonic Labyrinthine Reflex (TLR) starts to integrate, you will begin to see improvements and changes in your child's development. To make the changes that are needed, however, you should practice the home exercises your occupational therapist assigns for at least 10 minutes per day. If, after six to eight weeks of therapy, you do not see any changes in your child, please contact your occupational therapist. You know your child best and will notice the main areas of growth or/and lack thereof. To help guide you through the process, here are some things you can look for and observe during your child's treatment:

*   Your child may become a lot more coordinated or start to show improvement in movement activities.

*   Your child may begin to tumble and roll with ease.

*   Your child's seated and standing posture will begin to improve

*   Your child may become stronger and more alert.

*   Your child's visual skill, reading and copying from a board may start to improve.

> **Note:** If visual skills are an issue, please consult a trained vision therapist.

- Your child may be a lot more interested in joining a game or participating in sports (increased confidence).

- If your child is in a swim class, you might see improvement and less overall hesitation to get in the water and swim.

- Your child's eye-hand and eye-foot coordination may start to improve (e.g., able to catch, throw and kick a ball).

- Your child may become more focused and less distracted.

- You might see improvement in your child's walking stride and standing posture (i.e., will move from chin tucked out with slouched back, to shoulders down/relaxed, with straight back, and chin tucked in).

- Your child's balance, muscle tone and stability may improve.

- Your child may become stronger (e.g., better trunk and core muscle strength).

TABLE #3: TONIC LABYRINTHINE REFLEX (TLR) INTEGRATION EXERCISE LOG

	Tonic Labyrinthine Reflex (TLR) Integration Exercises	Date Introduced	Date Given to Parents	Date Mastered
1				
2				
3				
4				
5				
6				
7				
8				
9				
10				
11				
12				
13				
14				

15				
16				
17				
18				
19				
20				
21				
22				
23				
24				
25				
26				
27				
28				
29				
30				
31				

32				
33				
34				
35				

Visit https://ritp.info/tlr-book for a downloadable version.

GLOSSARY

Asymmetrical Tonic Neck Reflex (ATNR): is a primitive reflex pattern that usually emerges in utero, near 18 weeks, is fully present at birth, and integrates approximately six months after birth. The ATNR is an involuntary movement reaction in response to the head turning to the right or to the left. When the head turns to one side, the ATNR causes the arm and leg the head turns toward to extend (stretch) while the opposite arm and leg flex (bend).

Agonist Muscles: muscle groups that contract together to create a desired action.

Antagonist Muscles: muscle groups that move against agonist muscles to produce an opposite force.

Auditory Localization: the ability to perceive and locate from where a sound is coming.

Binaural Hearing: the ability to hear with both ears equally.

Binocular Vision: also known as **eye teaming**, binocular vision is the ability to use both eyes to focus on an object to see a clear, singular image.

Body Awareness: is the understanding of where our body parts are in space and how they are moving.

Convergence: an inward movement of both eyes to focus on a single object; also called "binocular vision."

Cross-lateral Movements: any movement pattern that requires the use of both parts of the body to coordinate and move simultaneously to execute a purposeful pattern of movements by crossing the midline. Activities such as walking, running and crawling, require us to cross the midline of the body.

Divergence: an outward movement of both eyes to focus on an object further away; also called "binocular" vision.

Eye-hand Coordination: also known as **hand-eye coordination**, is the ability to process visual input to guide the hands to achieve a specific task (e.g., reaching and grasping).

Eye Teaming: also known as binocular vision, is the ability to use both eyes to focus on an object to see a clear singular image.

Extension: straightening of body parts.

Flexion: bending of body parts.

Moro Reflex: is a primitive reflex pattern that typically emerges in utero and integrates approximately four months after birth. Moro Reflex is an involuntary reaction to what the brain perceives as an outside threat. The threatening stimuli can come in via touch, sound or the feeling of being dropped, which creates a sense of falling. When the child senses these sensations, the reflex causes the fanning and clenching of fingers, spreading or extending the extremities, followed by a quick flexion of extremities, and crying or anger.

Motor Learning: is a neurological ability to learn new movement skills through practice and repetition.

Motor Planning: is the ability to understand, plan and execute multiple-step movement activities in the correct order.

Movement Overflow: also known as "motor overflow," is an involuntary movement (motor) pattern observed during voluntary activity. For example, the tongue sticking out or facial grimace during handwriting or balancing activities.

Primitive Reflexes: are involuntary movement patterns that are present at birth and become dormant or "integrated" before the child reaches 12 months of age. Most reflexes become integrated into a pattern of movement after infancy, so more mature and voluntary movements can emerge.

Proprioceptive Input: is an internal sense of **body awareness** that comes from our joints, muscles, tendons and connective tissues when we move or bear weight on our limbs.

Retained Reflex: is a term used to refer to primitive reflexes that are active in the body when they should have been inhibited (dormant).

Right/Left Discrimination: is an internal or external spatial perception, interpretation, and differentiation of sensory information that originated from the left and right sides of the body.

Rooting Reflex: is a primitive reflex pattern that typically emerges in utero and integrates approximately three to four months after birth. When the baby's mouth or cheek is stroked or touched, the head turns toward the stroke, and the mouth opens in search of stimuli. If the mouth finds something to grab, the mouth closes over it, and the sucking motion begins.

Palmar (Grasp) Reflex: is a primitive reflex pattern that emerges in utero at approximately 11 weeks gestation and integrates approximately 12 months after birth. When the infant's palm is stroked or touched at the base of the fingers, the fingers close into a firm grasp starting from the pinky finger.

Peripheral Vision: is the eyes' ability to use side vision while gazing straight ahead.

Postural Reflex: are mature patterns of responses that control balance, motor coordination and sensory-motor development.

Saccade Eye Movement: is the eye's ability to accurately jump back and forth between targets.

Sensory Integration: is a term, developed by Jean Ayers, which explains how the brain receives, perceives and reacts to sensory information either from inside or outside the body. She defines sensory integration as *"the neurological process that organizes sensation from one's own body and from the environment and makes it possible to use the body effectively within the environment."*

Smooth Pursuit: is the eye's ability to smoothly and accurately track a moving object or follow a line.

Spatial Orientation: is the brain's ability to orient the body to the ground with or without vision.

Spinal Galant Reflex: is a primitive reflex pattern present in the womb and also present at birth that integrates at approximately 9-12 months of age. When the right or left side of the back below the waist is stroked or touched, this reflex causes the child to side-bend toward the same direction.

Symmetrical Tonic Neck Reflex (STNR): is a primitive reflex pattern that usually emerges in utero and continues to develop after birth. It becomes active at approximately six months of age and starts to integrate at approximately ten months. The STNR is an involuntary reaction to a downward and upward movement of the head. There are two STNR positions. Position 1 is a downward head movement, which causes the elbows to flex and the legs to extend. Position 2 is an upward head movement (also called Sphinx Position), which causes the elbows to extend and the legs to flex.

Tonic Labyrinthine Reflex (TLR): is a primitive reflex pattern that usually emerges in utero and continues to develop after birth. The TLR is an involuntary reaction to the forward and backward movement of the head. There are two types: **TLR Forward** occurs when the head is in front of the spine, causing the arms and legs to flex and tuck inward. **TLR Backward** occurs when the head is behind the line of the spine, causing the arms and the legs to extend, and the back to arch and stiffen.

Vestibular Sense: is the body's sense of balance and movement.

Visual Tracking: is the ability to maintain a visual gaze on a moving object or a predictable line while reading.

Visual Discrimination: is the ability to recognize details in what is being seen while identifying similarities and differences.

RESOURCES

Active Baby, Healthy Brain: 135 Fun Exercises to Maximize Your Child's Brain Development from Birth through age 5½, by Margaret Sasse.

Assessing Neuromotor Readiness for Learning: The INPP Developmental Screening Test and School Intervention Programme, by Sally Goddard.

Integration of Infant Dynamic and Postural Reflex Patterns-MNRI (Masgutova Neurosensorimotor Reflex Integration), by Svetlana Rihanna Masgutova Ketubah, PhD.

Masgutova Neurosensorimotor Reflex Integration programs https://masgutovamethod.com/

Movement That Heals, by Harald Blomberg, MD.

Neuromotor Immaturity in Children and Adults: The INPP Screening Test for Clinicians and Health Practitioners, by Sally Goddard.

Parents' Guide to Masgutova Neurosensorimotor Reflex Integration (MNRI), by Svetlana Masgutova, PhD & Denis Masgutova.

Reflexes, Learning and Behavior, by Sally Goddard.

The Misunderstood Child: Understanding and Coping with Your Child's Learning Disabilities, by Larry B. Silver, MD.

The Out-of-Sync Child: Recognizing and Coping with Sensory Integration Dysfunction, by Carol Stock Kranowitz, MA.

The Rhythmic Movement Method: A Revolutionary Approach to Improved Health and Well-Being, by Harald Blomberg, MD.

The Symphony of Reflexes: Interventions for Human Development, Autism, CP, and Other Neurological Disorders, by Bonnie L. Brandes, Med.

Medical Dictionary: https://medical-dictionary.thefreedictionary.com/

ABOUT THE AUTHOR

Kokeb Girma McDonald is a pediatric occupational therapist and the founder of Polaris Therapy. She is the mother of two wonderful children, and has extensive professional experience working with young people of all ages and backgrounds, since 2004. Recognizing the need for practical and universally accessible primitive-reflex-integration programs, Kokeb created Integrating Primitive Reflexes Through Play and Exercise book series and online courses to empower and reassure frustrated parents, and to offer fellow professionals a tool to expand their clinical reach. Kokeb's formal education includes a Bachelor's of Science in Occupational Therapy, and a Master's of Science in Health Care Administration, Management, and Change in Health Care Options. She also has additional training in the Masgutova Neurosensorimotor Reflex Integration (MNRI), Integrated Listening Systems (iLs), Interactive Metronome (IM), and Rhythmic Movement Training (RMTi).

Make a Difference
by leaving a review!

Instructions: Scan the code above, scroll to the bottom of the Amazon product page, and click the "Write a Review" button

Your review helps Reflex Integration Through Play™ reach more parents, therapists, and teachers in need!

I appreciate all of your feedback and love hearing what you have to say. These books are for you! We need your help to make our series better. Thank you for all your support!

Kokeb Mcdonald

OTR/L & Author

Made in United States
Orlando, FL
13 August 2024